Pictured Key
Nature Series

How To Know

THE SEAWEEDS

An illustrated manual for identifying the more
common Marine Algae of both our Atlantic
and Pacific coasts with numerous aids for their
study.

E. YALE DAWSON, Ph.D.

D1261063

WM. C. BROWN COMPANY PUBLISHERS
Dubuque, Iowa

Copyright 1956 by H.E. Jaques

ISBN 0-697-04885-3 (Paper)
ISBN 0-697-04882-9 (Cloth)

Library of Congress Catalog Card Number: 56-14426

THE PICTURED-KEY NATURE SERIES

How To Know The—

AQUATIC PLANTS, Prescott, 1969
BEETLES, Jaques, 1951
BUTTERFLIES, Ehrlich, 1961
CACTI, Dawson, 1963
EASTERN LAND SNAILS, Burch, 1962
ECONOMIC PLANTS, Jaques, 1948, 1958
FALL FLOWERS, Cuthbert, 1948
FRESHWATER ALGAE, Prescott, 1954, 1970
FRESHWATER FISHES, Eddy, 1957, 1969
GRASSES, Pohl, 1953, 1968
GRASSHOPPERS, Helfer, 1963, 1972
IMMATURE INSECTS, Chu, 1949
INSECTS, Jaques, 1947
LAND BIRDS, Jaques, 1947
LICHENS, Hale, 1969
LIVING THINGS, Jaques, 1946
MAMMALS, Booth, 1949, 1970
MARINE ISOPOD CRUSTACEANS, Schultz, 1969
MOSSES AND LIVERWORTS, Conard, 1944, 1956
NON-GILLED FLESHY FUNGI, Smith-Smith, 1973
PLANT FAMILIES, Jaques, 1948
POLLEN AND SPORES, Kapp, 1969
PROTOZOA, Jahn, 1949
ROCKS AND MINERALS, Helfer, 1970
SEAWEEDS, Dawson, 1956
SPIDERS, Kaston, 1953, 1972
SPRING FLOWERS, Cuthbert, 1943, 1949
TAPEWORMS, Schmidt, 1970
TREMATODES, Schell, 1970
TREES, Miller-Jaques, 1946, 1972
WATER BIRDS, Jaques-Ollivier, 1960
WEEDS, Wilkinson-Jaques, 1959, 1972
WESTERN, TREES, Baerg, 1955, 1973

Printed in United States of America   12/73

FOREWORD

T HE most recent comprehensive monograph of the marine algae of the combined Atlantic and Pacific coasts of the United States is a splendid one, printed in quarto and with some of the finest colored plates in the literature. The work is the more impressive when one realizes that the author, W. H. Harvey, did his field work without the aid of an automobile or a motor driven boat, made his microscopic examinations without the aid of an electric light, and made his own drawings on lithographic limestone. The time,—a century ago. From the four hundred odd kinds of algae enumerated by Harvey from the American shores the number of known species has grown to about two thousand, with many still to be recognized and named. Yet, with all of this expansion of knowledge there has come no single modern monograph treating the North American seaweeds. More conspicuous to many is the lack of any handbook designed to aid the amateur and the elementary student in identifying the commoner kinds of marine algae. It is toward filling a part of this need that this little book is offered.

Inasmuch as the coasts of the United States are so very extensive and the range of habitats and climates so varied, both on the Atlantic and Pacific sides of the continent, a treatment of all of the species of seaweeds in a small volume is impossible. Space does not permit even a representative illustration for each of the many genera. However, our purpose is to provide a useful tool for the elementary student of phycology, and with his needs in mind a selection has been made of those plants which he is most likely to encounter wherever he may be along the coasts of the United States. Algae which are very small, or are of rare or localized occurrence, are omitted. Likewise, in the preparation of the key an effort has been made to present those features which apply to the mature, well developed plants rather than to juvenile or stunted forms which are not characteristic.

The author does not expect that the student will be completely satisfied with the treatment, for occasionally there will be times when the plant at hand is not to be found in this book, or when the illustration does not look very much like a particular specimen brought in for study. On the other hand he does hope that this handbook will serve the student in a large majority of cases to determine the names of the seaweeds he has collected, wherever he lives or travels along American Shores.

With few exceptions the illustrations have been drawn by the author from actual specimens. The preparation of these was greatly facilitated by the herbarium material available at the Allan Hancock Foundation, University of Southern California.

Los Angeles, California
October, 1955

E. Yale Dawson

Almost every one who walks along an ocean beach wonders about the plant debris left by the waves. The need for a book offering ready identification of the more evident species of marine algae is apparent.

It is truly timely that Dr. Dawson, with his splendid experience with these interesting plants, has given us this much-needed identification manual.

Editor

CONTENTS

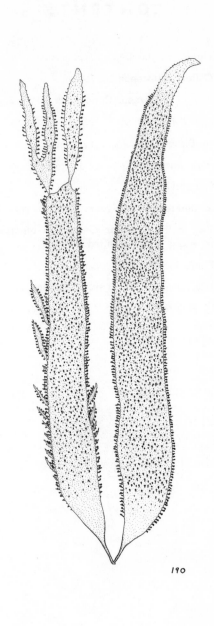

190

THE VEGETATION OF THE SEA

OUR-FIFTHS of the surface of our globe is covered by salt water, and since all of the multitudes of animal inhabitants of this vast aquatic environment are ultimately dependent upon the photosynthetic plants, we may say that in one sense the marine plants are the most important of all the groups of organisms on earth.

In the sea, extremes of climate are modulated by the water medium, and the vastly predominant environment is one of monotonous darkness and cold. Accordingly, the diversity of living things on the whole is less than on the land, and while some groups are poorly represented, others are entirely lacking. Thus, whereas the highly developed mammals are sparsely represented in the sea and the insects not at all, in the marine vegetation the seed plants and fungi are few and the ferns and mosses absent. On the other hand, some of the phyla of organisms present in the sea are absent on land, or much less richly developed there. This is true of the several groups of plants known as algae of which the great bulk of the marine vegetation is composed.

With the exception of the bacteria and of a few parasitic and saprophytic fungi, virtually all of the marine plants are autophytic, that is to say, independent and capable of providing their own food by means of photosynthesis. To do this they need two primary raw materials, namely, water, which is seldom in short supply, and CO_2. Energy for the process of photosynthesis must be supplied by sunlight which, however, is largely absent in the sea. Most of the marine environment is totally lacking in sunlight which penetrates, even in the most exceptionally clear water, only to as much as three or four hundred feet. Accordingly, these autophytic plants are restricted in the

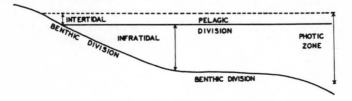

Fig. 1. Diagram of the general habitats of the plants of the sea.

immensity of the oceans to a relatively thin layer of illuminated surface water and to the narrow intertidal and infratidal fringe within this photic zone. In these places, however, they may be remarkably abundant.

The general habitats of the plants of this illuminated portion of the sea may be diagrammed as in Figure 1. The vegetable inhabitants of the pelagic division, that is, of the water mass itself, are the phytoplankton, while those of the benthic division, or the sea floor, are what we may call the seaweeds, or attached algae.

The phytoplankton consists of free floating, unattached plants which move about only as their water medium moves. With few exceptions they are unicellular forms of microscopic size requiring quite high magnification to render them visible (Fig. 2). Despite their small size, their habitat in the surface waters of all of the oceans is so vast and their numbers so great that they actually account for more than 95% of the vegetation of the sea.

Fig. 2. Some representatives of the phytoplankton.
A. A dinoflagellate, *Ceratium*. B. A diatom, *Planktoniella*. C. A coccolithophore, *Pontosphaera*. D. A silicoflagellate, *Distephanus*. All are drawn to the same scale (X 225) and are shown against a heavy outline which represents the point of a dissecting needle.

Several different kinds of organisms make up the phytoplankton (Fig. 2) of which may be mentioned the diatoms, the pigmented dinoflagellates, the silicoflagellates, the coccolithophores and a few blue-green algae. Most abundant of these constituents are the diatoms, of which several million may sometimes occur in a single quart of sea water. These are unicellular members of the division Chrysophyta whose protoplasm secretes a beautifully sculptured, bivalved, silicious shell (Fig. 3). The shell is basically like a pill-box in structure, but often is marvelously modified for flotation where perpetuation of a species depends upon the ability to remain in the photic zone.

Because of the tremendous numbers of these tiny plants in the sea, and of the perpetual rain of their insoluble silicious shells on the bottom, great deposits accumulate which may be hundreds of feet deep. Some of these deposits have been raised above sea level and form the beds of diatomaceous earth such as occur at Lompoc, California, and are exploited commercially for the making of fine scouring compounds.

On account of the very small size of the phytoplankton organisms, the high magnifications needed for viewing them, and the special methods required in collecting, preserving and examining them, they do not lend themselves readily to study by the amateur or elementary student and will not be treated further in this account.

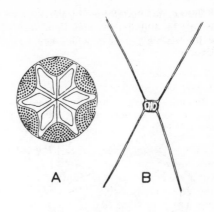

Fig. 3. Examples of two different forms of planktonic diatoms.

A. *Asterolampra*, a broad, flat, disc-like form. B. *Chaetoceras*, a very small-bodied form with long hair-like modifications of the silicious frustule to aid in flotation. Both X 200.

3

Unlike the vegetation of the surface water masses of the oceans, that of the illuminated sea floor and of the shore consists mostly of readily visible plants of which some reach large size. Among these, to be sure, there are many microscopic forms, including littoral diatoms (Fig. 4) and minute blue-green algae (Fig. 5) which sometimes form more or less conspicuous macroscopic colonies. These must be neglected here, however, in favor of the three main groups of seaweeds with which we need be concerned, namely, the Green Algae (Chlorophyta), the Brown Algae (Phaeophyta) and the Red Algae (Rhodophyta). The seed plants, although of very few kinds, are exceedingly abundant in many coastal habitats and will be accounted for and illustrated at the end of this book.

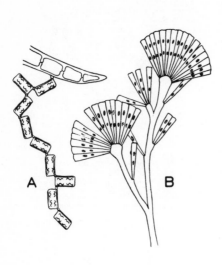

Fig. 4. Two examples of different forms of littoral diatoms.
A. An epiphytic, chain form, *Grammatophora*.
B. A stalked form, *Licmophora*.

These three groups of algae which make up the vast majority of the seaweeds are named because of the predominant colors which their members commonly assume, and are technically distinguished by the chemistry of their pigments. Thus, the Green Algae are characteristically pigmented only by green chlorophyll, while the Brown and Red Algae have their chlorophyll masked by other pigments. On this account the Green Algae almost always appear green in color, while the others may be neither brown nor red, depending upon the relative dominance of the chlorophyll or of the masking pigments. When the color is such as to leave one in doubt as to the group to which a plant may belong, other characters must be taken into account in identification. Because of the difficulty experienced by most students in recognizing according to color the main group to which a seaweed belongs, the present key treats all of the Green, Brown and Red Algae together, separating them from each other without particular regard to color.

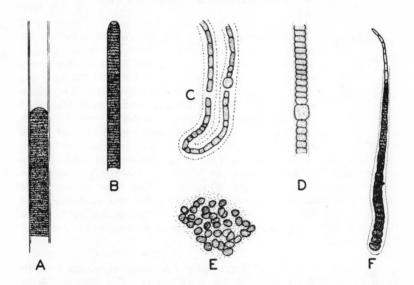

Fig. 5. Some examples of Blue-Green Algae.
A. *Lyngbya* sp., X 193.   B. *Oscillatoria* sp., X 200.   C. *Brachytrichia* sp., X 275.
D. *Hormothamnion* sp., X 330.   E. *Entophysalis* sp., X 500.   F. *Calothrix* sp., X 275.

HOW TO COLLECT SEAWEEDS

EAWEEDS rarely grow in the free floating state, but instead are fixed firmly at their bases and remain stationary throughout life. Only in the Sargasso Sea northeast of the Caribbean and in the Gulf of Thailand are there sizable quantities of the brown alga *Sargassum* (see Fig. 141) living in the free floating state. Elsewhere the seaweeds grow attached to the bottom or to each other. Since an unstable bottom such as one of sand or mud is unfavorable to the attachment of seaweeds, they are usually absent from such substrates except in quiet bays and lagoons where agitation is slight. On surfy shores the algae are essentially confined to rocky places where their firm attachments give them resistance to wave shock. This is especially true along the rugged, wave-swept Pacific Coast where the collector rarely encounters the richly vegetated quiet bays or estuaries such as occur so frequently along the Atlantic Coast.

The coasts of the United States offer a diversity of marine habitats scarcely equalled by those of any other nation. This diversity is so great that no single set of directions can be made suitable for a collector among the Florida keys, another on Cape Cod and another on Puget Sound. One can only make a few general remarks and suggestions, leaving the rest to the adjustability and ingenuity of the American individual wherever he may be.

At the outset it is clear that one must get to the seashore to collect seaweeds, but this is not always as simple as it may seem. Many of our rocky shores abounding in algae are subject to surf of varying intensity whereby collecting is made difficult or impossible except at times of lowest water. Accordingly, it is necessary to select a suitable time for the collecting trip, depending upon the state of the tide. Tide tables issued by the U. S. Coast and Geodetic Survey or by various sporting goods houses for the use of fishermen should be consulted for the times of suitable low water. The so called "minus tides" are the best, but even with only moderately low water much can be done if the surf is not too severe. The collector should plan to begin work at the shore at least two hours before the time of low tide in order to work the clearer water of the falling tide and to select his material successively from higher to lower levels while the plants are freshly exposed and still wet and unshriveled from desiccation.

Collecting equipment on a rocky shore should consist of a pail or two for carrying the specimens, a quantity of plastic bags for separating the larger species, and a number of small, screw-cap vials provided with 3% formalin into which small but important specimens may be preserved from loss or mixing. For removing small plants from rock surfaces a heavy knife or other scaping tool is used, while encrusting forms which adhere too firmly may be obtained by using a geologist's hammer for cracking off pieces of the supporting rock.

At the upper levels one will find a number of minute species on the exposed rock surfaces, including various crustose forms which the initiate may overlook unless they are pointed out to him. Lower down, depending upon the amount of exposure to desiccation, one will encounter larger and smaller

Collecting Tools.

fleshy, clumping forms grading into the densely matted turfs, or heavy, continuous beds of algae at the lowest tide levels. It will not be enough to look superficially over the array of seaweeds to obtain a good collection, for many species will be hidden under others or will occur only in particular pools, in certain shaded crannies, along the edges of surging tideways, or on the exposed faces of outermost rocks subject to the heaviest surf. Many species will be found growing only as epiphytes or as parasites on other, larger species and should be obtained by selection of suitable portions of the host plants. Algal turfs consisting of many species may be brought back as a mass to be examined for their individual constituents in the laboratory. At lowest water level the collector will profit by wading out (in hip boots in cold areas) to look under overhanging rocks, in crannies and pools for the various species which can endure only momentary exposure to the atmosphere.

When the tide has begun to flow one must hasten to finish the work at low levels before retracing steps inward. With the incoming tide time may be taken to seek special pools and rocky habitats at higher levels which have been passed over before, and there to find additional species. Shaded cliffs subject to spray, the walls of sea caves, the under edges of rocks in tide pools, high, warm pools polluted by guano, and other such diverse habitats will all yield different species. Even pieces of dead shell or coral may exhibit a greenish cast indicating the presence of boring green algae.

After the selection of the attached algae from the intertidal rocks has been completed there is yet another source of specimens which should not be passed by. Especially at times of unfavorable tides one

7

may profit much from examining the beach drift which often accumulates in quantity in coves or along sand beaches adjoining rocky areas. It is among these cast specimens that many of the species of the deeper, infratidal waters may be found and selected with much greater ease than through the use of a boat and dredge. If driftweed is examined after a storm while the material is still fresh and has not been exposed long to the bleaching and drying action of the sun and air, many specimens in good condition may be selected.

Apart from rocky shore habitats the algologist finds many other situations in which seaweeds may be found. Many areas in which surf is light or absent, such as the sandy or muddy shores of bays, lagoons and estuaries, will yield specimens. Such quiet habitats are especially well populated in tropical regions, and within the range of the mangrove the algal flora of its roots is an interesting one which should not be overlooked. The piling of wharves and the rock or concrete of artificial breakwaters will yield many species. Indeed, along the vast sandy stretches of the Gulf of Mexico, these will be the principal algal habitats. Even mobile objects may have their seaweed floras. Thus, boat hulls will yield several species as may also the backs of sea turtles and several kinds of crabs. Particular species have even been found attached to the intersegmental grooves of isopods parasitic on certain fishes.

Beyond the level of low tide, and apart from those cast ashore in drift, the algae of infratidal waters must be obtained by means of diving or by some manner of dredging. In very quiet, surfless waters a collector may wade about observing the bottom by means of a glass-bottom bucket and reaching specimens with ease. In depths of more than three feet, observation is best afforded by a face plate and collections made by placing specimens in a skiff as they are obtained by the diver. In depths of more than ten feet the diver must be provided with breathing apparatus in order to spend the time below the surface necessary for the selection of specimens. The "aqua-lung" has recently become popular with skin-divers and its use may readily be learned in most any area of warm, quiet water where these sportsmen thrive. In colder waters the diver must be provided with the standard heavy diving suit and helmet. It is this heavy suit which is normally used by the commercial seaweed collectors who harvest *Gelidium* and other agar-yielding seaweeds from the infratidal beds along the Pacific Coast.

Apart from those areas where skin-diving may be done comfortably, the collecting of infratidal algae is best accomplished by the use of a dredge handled by a powered winch on shipboard. The use of various devices of this sort is described by Sverdrup, Johnson &

Fleming, The Oceans, Prentice-Hall, Inc., 1942, and may be observed on ships operated by the several oceanographic institutions of the country.

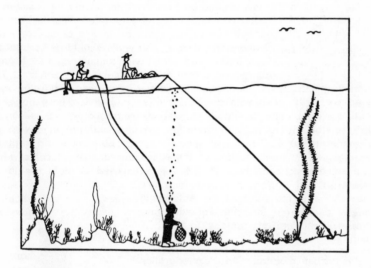

HARVESTING *GELIDIUM*.

PRESERVATION OF SEAWEED COLLECTIONS

 HEN the day's collecting has been completed the specimens should be preserved as quickly as possible to prevent unnecessary deterioration. This is best accomplished at the shore by means of one or more five-gallon tin cans. Sea water should be brought up in a bucket and mixed with commercial 40% formaldehyde to obtain approximately a 3% solution. The various plastic bags into which specimens have been separated may then be partly filled with the preservative and tied. These bags, together with bulkier materials as well as small bottles of specimens may all be placed in the can in preservative and provided with an appropriate label. The tin of specimens may be closed and kept for months without deterioration of the specimens or loss of color, while the same specimens kept in glass jars exposed to light would be bleached and largely worthless in a few days. The tin may, indeed, be sealed with solder and boxed for shipment with ease and without fear of damage to the contents.

Of utmost importance in the preparation of any collection is the provision of adequate field data in the field collection notebook, and the careful preparation of labels. For this purpose all pertinent observations on the character of the habitat, size and aspect of the various dominant species, the major associations, water temperature, substrate type, exposure, etc., should be recorded before leaving the field. These data should be incorporated in the permanent book of field notes, in which a consecutive series of collection numbers is tabulated.

A Dredge.

Upon return to the laboratory the preparation of specimens may begin at once, although it is preferable to leave the material in preservative for a few days time. This applies particularly to certain species which when fresh are damaged by being immersed in tap water, but which are not harmed by the same treatment after having remained a few days or weeks in the formalin- sea water solution.

It will be found most convenient to obtain one or more large porcelain trays and a number of wide-mouthed jars of various sizes into which to sort the specimens. After quickly washing with tap water the various species should be separated into the jars, each species receiving a number which is listed in the field notebook beneath the field data previously recorded. Of each of the species, especially the smaller or more delicate forms, appropriate portions should be placed in small vials (4 dram shell vials) for future use in making preparations for microscopic examination. These, of course, also receive in each case the same field number assigned to the remaining material of a given species.

After the segregation of all of the species into separate containers the drying may begin. Two methods may be employed depending upon the nature of the specimens. Crustose specimens which have been brought from the shore along with pieces of their substrate may be dried directly in the air and preserved in the dry state in small boxes of suitable size. Articulated, calcareous algae which are so fragile and (or) so three dimensional as to suffer badly from pressing, should be treated in the same way, or, preferably, soaked for several days or weeks in a solution of about 40% glycerine in 3% formalin before being dried and placed in the small boxes. Most of the remainder of the algae may be dried in a standard plant press.

Inasmuch as the algal specimens should ultimately be mounted on standard 11½ by 16½ herbarium paper,[1] whole sheets or suitably sized pieces of this paper may be used for the next step which is the backing of the specimen as it is floated out for drying.

Mounting may best be done in a broad, shallow tray large enough to accommodate a full size herbarium sheet. The sheet of paper to be used in each instance should be immersed in water in the bottom of the tray. The water should be of the least depth suitable for floating out the particular specimen at hand and spreading it on the paper. After the plant has been spread out in a natural appearing manner on its suitably sized sheet in the water tray, the sheet should be lifted carefully from one side to allow the water to drain off gradually and to leave the specimen spread out and undisturbed on the sheet. A device for affecting this drainage may be made from a piece of galvanized sheet metal by bending down the corners to form short legs. These will permit the middle to be depressed slightly for spreading a specimen and released to allow the water to drain off evenly.

---

1. This and other herbarium supplies, press materials, paste, packets, etc., may be obtained from herbarium supply houses such as Bonestell & Company, San Francisco, California; General Biological Supply House, 8200 South Hayne Ave., Chicago 20, Ill., or Ward's Natural Science Establishment, 3000 Ridge Road East, Rochester 9, N. Y.

The sheet or card bearing the spread specimen may be placed directly on a dry felt in the press and covered either with a piece of cloth or a piece of waxed paper. Cloth will serve best for drying coarse, succulent specimens, while the waxed paper will prove more satisfactory for smaller forms and especially very lubricous or muci-laginous ones. Very coarse specimens need not be spread on paper at all, but arranged between cloths in the press. After drying they may be mounted on the herbarium sheets by means of straps. Each specimen sheet should bear the collection number assigned to the particular species in the field note book.

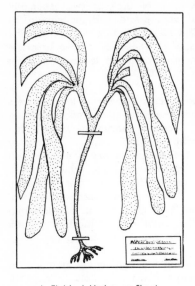

A Finished Herbarum Sheet.

When the spreading has been completed and the last felt drier has been placed over a specimen, the press should be strapped up with the application of considerable pressure. It is necessary to prevent the specimens from shrinking or curling during the drying process and to accomplish the drying in the shortest possible time. This may best be done by frequent changing of the driers,—at least once a day. The specimens should not be subjected to heat, as by placing the press in an oven, but, rather, dehydrated by frequent replacement of the wet driers with warm, dry ones. In changing the driers the first wet one on top should be removed and a dry one placed over the specimen, then, by insertion of one hand beneath the next lower wet felt while the other is placed on top, the whole layer may be lifted and turned upside down without disturbing the specimens or the cloth or waxed paper covering them. If this process is repeated quickly for each sheet and the pressure promptly reapplied in the press, good specimens will result in which a large proportion will adhere to the paper satisfactorily by means of their own mucilage. Drying will usually take from two days for delicate specimens to a week for coarse ones. It will usually be more quickly and satisfactorily accomplished after killing the specimens in formalin than otherwise. Care must be taken to be sure the drying is complete before removal of specimens from the press, for otherwise shrinkage of the specimen and consequent wrinkling and curling of the paper backing will result.

In the preparation of the marine algae herbarium it will be found necessary to provide for the storage of several different kinds of preservations. The fleshy species which lend themselves to pressing and mounting on herbarium sheets may be handled in the same way as are terrestrial plants. Those which have adhered well to backing sheets during the drying process may be mounted by pasting to standard herbarium sheets. Tin paste or standard herbarium paste should be used. Rubber cement, plastic cement, staples, etc., are not satisfactory. Coarser specimens which are dried free of backing may be fixed to herbarium sheets by means of paste or by strips of gummed cloth. When the herbarium label, (Fig. 6) properly inscribed, has been pasted to the lower right hand corner of the sheet the plant is ready for filing. If portions of the specimen have been retained in liquid preservative, this should be indicated somewhere on the sheet for future reference.

MARINE ALGAE OF CALIFORNIA

Locality: La Jolla, California

  June 1, 1946

Habitat: In deep shade at base of cliffs on southwest side of bay, among boulders subjected to heavy surf. Essentially sublittoral growth conditions. Temp. 18.8° C. at 5 a.m.

Collected by E. Yale Dawson   No.

  det. by

Fig. 6. A Sample Algal Specimen Label.

Liquid preserved specimens usually may be kept in dilute formalin for months or a few years without difficulty, but for long periods of time 65 to 70% ethyl alcohol seems to be more satisfactory. A convenient procedure is to keep the small bits of preserved material in 4 dram shell vials in the one-gross boxes in which they are sold. They may be cross-referenced (indexed) on the herbarium sheets by means of reference to consecutive numbers written on the corks. More permanent filing of these is accomplished by placing them within air tight, glass capped, pint mason jars.

Bulky specimens, especially calcareous forms and crustose species adhering to rocks, shells, etc., may best be kept in small boxes fitting into standardized cardboard trays. The trays may be numbered and the labeled specimens referred to by means of cross-reference sheets in the herbarium file.

Specimens which are too small for convenient mounting on herbarium sheets may be placed in small packets affixed to the sheet, or, if very small and delicate, mounted whole on slides and then cross-indexed. Inasmuch as the preparation of slides for study and reference is of great importance in algology, it seems well to explain here an easy method suitable for the majority of cases.

Permanent slides may readily be made of most species and for most general morphological purposes by using the ordinary crystal clear variety of Karo corn syrup. Material preserved either in formalin or alcohol may be prepared after washing in water. The specimen is first stained either with analin blue or acid fuchsin on a slide by adding a little aqueous stain, acidifying and then washing with a drop or two of distilled water. After the excess water is drawn off with blotting paper, Karo syrup, diluted to 50-60% with distilled water, is applied and the slide left open to the air in a dust free place over night. The next day, after the first drop of dilute Karo has dried down so that excessive plasmolysis (shrinking) of the cells of the specimen has been avoided, another drop of more concentrated Karo (about 80%) is added and the cover slip applied to complete the preparation which is self sealing. The Karo dries around the edges within a few days and although the slide should not be allowed to stand on edge for a considerably longer period, it may otherwise be handled with ease. In the case of transections or of species with a dense structure of small cells, plasmolysis is not appreciable, and these may be mounted directly in 80% Karo. Very small bubbles usually will form gradually under the cover slip as the drying proceeds, but these rarely affect the usefulness of the preparation. In the writer's experience such slides have shown no appreciable deterioration after 15 years of storage.

For making sections of many specimens a freezing microtome will prove most desirable, but in the absence of such an instrument good sections can be made by hand with a razor blade after a little practice. This is most easily accomplished by using dried specimens, for in the majority of cases such sections will expand in a drop of water to very nearly their normal size and shape. If they do not, a little heat usually helps. Stubborn cases usually respond to the addition of potassium hydroxide and heat. The most convenient cutting method is that whereby the specimen fragment is held with a finger on a white card under a dissecting microscope of 6 to 10 power and sliced with the blade against a finger nail for support and guide.

Calcareous algae present special difficulties in sectioning and must be decalcified and dehydrated with alcohol, embedded in paraffin and sectioned on a rotary microtome. Sectioning and staining procedures may be found in accounts of botanical microtechnique, such ¬s Johansen's Plant Microtechnique, McGraw Hill & Co., 1940.

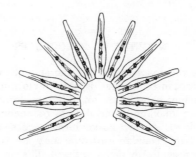

WHAT TO LOOK FOR

N beginning a study of the seaweeds the student usually expresses surprise that the members of a single family or genus appear to be entirely different from each other, while, on the other hand, members of completely unrelated groups may look alike. This is so because his superficial examination of the plants has not permitted him to see the features by which the plants may be related or distinguished. It must be emphasized that for the beginner, who has as yet no acquaintanceship with the various forms, microscopic examination of the vegetative structure and also of the reproductive organs of the plants is essential to an understanding of them and to his success in the use of the key which follows.

VEGETATIVE STRUCTURES

Among these macroscopic marine algae with which we are dealing, the seaweeds, the protoplasm is always surrounded by a cell wall which may assume a multitude of different forms and which may range from thin to thick, and from rigid to gelatinous. In a great many of the smaller algae, or even larger forms whose thalli are finely dissected, much of the cellular structure may be observed simply by making a whole mount of a piece of the thallus on a slide. The larger and coarser forms, however, have such a dense structure that it is impossible to make out details of cellular structure unless thin, transparent sections are cut to show the organization of the cells in the plane desired.

Many of the delicate forms will show under the microscope that they are made up of a single row of cells constituting a uniseriate filament. Some such filaments are always unbranched, while others are branched in various ways. The diagrams in Fig. 7 show several different manners of branching which may be encountered.

Among uniseriate filaments, some will be encountered which have short cells, about as long as wide, while others will have elongated cells (See Figs. 96 and 97). Still others will exhibit only occasional cross walls, often only at the points of branching. These will be coenocytic forms of marine green algae in which the cells are multinucleate. Among these coenocytic green algae are a number of forms in which cross walls are rare or entirely lacking in the filaments, so that the entire plant consists of a variously ramified hollow tube. The famous *Valonia ventricosa* (See Fig. 13) consists essentially of a single large, multinucleate cell which may become as large as a hen's egg.

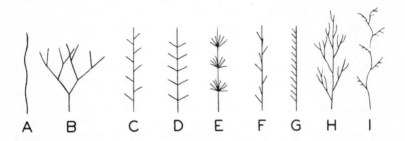

Fig. 7. Some examples of different kinds of branching in the marine algae. A. Unbranched (simple); B. Dichotomous C. Pinnate alternate; D. Pinnate opposite; E. Verticillate; F. Multifarious; G. Pectinate, or secund; H. Monopodial; I. Sympodial.

Other filamentous thalli will be found to be multiseriate, or made up of several rows, tiers or layers of cells. Sometimes it will be possible to interpret the structure satisfactorily by focusing through the more or less transparent external cells to observe the inner ones, but if there are more than two or three layers of cells involved it usually will require a cross section or longitudinal section to determine the cell forms and relationships. Such sections will often result in the discovery that the filament which appeared to be solid is actually a hollow tube, or that the central region contains a distinctive kind of cell structure which was invisible from the outside.

Coarser thalli will be found to be made up in a variety of different ways. Some quite large plants such as *Codium fragile* may consist entirely of branched, unseptate, coenocytic filaments, while slippery or gelatinous plants such as *Nemalion* often are similarly composed of branched filaments which are, however, regularly septate. Others, such as *Gracilaria*, show a firm, solid, compact structure of cells of increasing size from the outside inward. Many of the larger thalli, either cylindrical or flattened, show a differentiation of tissues whereby a parenchymatous medulla is enclosed by a filamentous cortex, or vice versa. In some of the giant kelps, such as *Nereocystis*, such specialized structures as sieve tubes comparable to those of higher plants occur.

It is often necessary to examine the apex of thallus branches to determine the manner of growth. The apex, also, is often so relatively
delicate that it permits observation of cellular structure which is obscured in the denser, older parts of the thallus (See Fig. 18). Growth
may occur in a variety of ways. In some uniseriate filaments, growth
may proceed by intercalary division of cells in any part, or in a
special region of the filament (See Fig. 106). In trichothallic growth
such intercalary divisions occur in multiseriate thalli at the base of one
or more apical hairs (See Fig. 19 and glossary for explanation of these
terms). Apical growth may occur in other ways, namely, by means
of a single apical cell which cuts off new cells from below, or by a
small or large number of cells forming a "fountain type" of apical
meristem (See Fig. 20), each cutting off cells from lower sides. Still
another manner of growth is observed in many complanate thalli in
which the actively dividing, meristematic cells lie along the margin
so that growth proceeds by expansion of the margins.

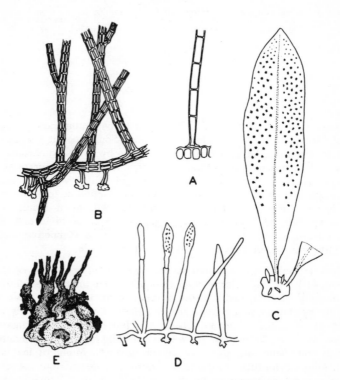

Fig. 8. Examples of various kinds of holdfasts. A. A simple, modified, basal cell
(Chaetomorpha); B. Unicellular rhizoids (Lophosiphonia); C. A solid basal disc (Grinnellia); D. Creeping stolons with adherent discs (Gelidium); E. A horny cone (Sargassum).

HOW TO KNOW THE SEAWEEDS

It will be worth while for the student to take particular notice of the apices of branches in the Red Algae, for in that group especially the characteristics of the apex will provide important clues for identification. He will find, for example, that the presence of a single apical cell is usually associated with the presence of a central axial filament and that the recognition of these and of other such features may be important in understanding the vegetative structure for the purpose of interpreting correctly the steps in the key.

It will become evident as experience is gained in making cross sections for the purpose of revealing the features of internal structure that young portions of a plant are much more satisfactory for sectioning than very old ones. The additional complications contributed by secondary growth of certain tissues often obscure the important basic features of structure. Accordingly, one should exercise some care in the selection of a suitable fragment for sectioning, or should repeat the operation on several different parts if difficulties are encountered in the first interpretation.

The manner of attachment to the substrate differs widely in the marine algae, from a holdfast consisting of a single modified basal cell, to various kinds of penetrating or entangling rhizoids, multicellular, adherent discs, creeping stolons, and massive clasping hapteres (Fig. 8). In many instances the kind of attachment constitutes an important generic or specific character, and identification may be impossible without a knowledge of it. Accordingly, it is important for the collector to obtain complete plants including the holdfast wherever possible, even if this may require breaking the rock upon which a specimen is growing.

REPRODUCTIVE STRUCTURES

UNLIKE the several seed-bearing marine flowering plants which are treated at the end of this book, the algae reproduce, with few exceptions, by means of microscopic spores. Although these spores themselves are very small, the reproductive structures which produce them are often large enough to be visible to the unaided eye and are useful in providing distinctive characters for classification purposes. For this reason the student should acquaint himself with some of the more general aspects of algal reproduction before endeavoring to identify his specimens.

The widespread misconception that the algae are "just simple, primitive plants" is quickly dispelled when one studies their marvel-

19

ously varied life histories and often exceedingly complex reproductive mechanisms. So varied are these that space is available here only for the presentation of a few generalizations and examples under each of the three major seaweed divisions. For more detailed information the student is referred to G. M. Smith's Cryptogamic Botany, Vol. 1, McGraw Hill & Co., and for a highly comprehensive account with full bibliography, to F. E. Fritsch's The Structure and Reproduction of the Algae, Volumes 1-2, Cambridge University Press.

THE GREEN ALGAE

Only about 10% of the Chlorophyta are marine, but among these a number of different orders are represented along with a considerable range in reproductive complexity. Both asexual and sexual reproduction occur. In some of the simpler filamentous forms reproduction

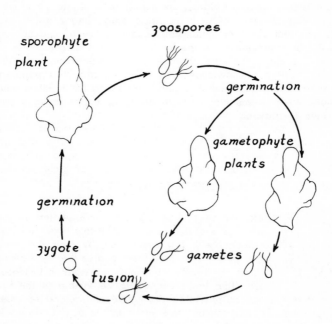

Fig. 9. Diagram of the Life Cycle of *Ulva*.

may occur mostly by fragmentation of the filament, but more commonly some kind of spore is produced which may germinate to produce a new plant. Two common kinds are the motile, flagella-bearing zoospore, and the non-motile aplanospore. These may be produced simply by a differentiation of the contents of a vegetative cell, or, if the structure producing the spores is in any way specialized and different from the ordinary vegetative cells, it is called a sporangium.

Sexual reproduction in the Green Algae involves a union of gametes which may be motile or non-motile. In the great majority of marine green algae the gametes are flagellated. When fusion occurs between those which are of equal size the species is called isogamous, while union of flagellated gametes of unequal size is characteristic of anisogamous species.

A type of life history which may be considered fairly representative of the many larger marine green algae is exemplified by *Ulva*, the sea lettuce. In *Ulva*, an alternation occurs between an asexual generation (sporophyte) producing quadri-flagellate zoospores, and a sexual generation (gametophyte) producing bi-flagellate gametes. The alternation is called isomorphic because the sporophyte plant (diploid generation) is essentially identical in external appearance with the gametophyte plant (haploid generation). The life cycle is diagrammed in Fig. 9.

Unlike *Ulva*, some genera of marine green algae bear special structures (sporangia and gametangia) for the production of their reproductive cells, but students will find that most genera of green algae can be recognized so readily from their vegetative form that reproductive organs usually need not be present for identification to that point. Specific identifications, on the other hand, may often require careful study of the reproductive organs and of the life history, sometimes even to the point of culturing the plants to obtain living spores and gametes for examination.

THE BROWN ALGAE

As a broad generalization it may be said that all the brown algae, with the exception of the Fucales, have an alternation of sporophyte and gametophyte generations, but among the greatly diversified forms of this large marine assemblage a number of variations and complications in the life histories are superimposed upon this fact. On the other hand, the beginning student will be relieved to know that the majority of the large brown, seaweeds have only one general kind of life cycle with which he needs first to become familiar. In this great majority of instances the large, macroscopic plant which is collectable in the field is the sporophyte generation which alternates with a microscopic gametophyte generation. The microscopic sexual plants are rarely detectable in nature and have been learned about through laboratory culture studies. Thus, among the brown algae treated in this account, with the exception of the orders Ectocarpales and Dictyotales, the plants encountered in the field will be of only one generation, namely, the sporophyte.

The life cycle of *Laminaria* is presented as an example of this prevalent heteromorphic type of alternation in which the two generations are dissimilar. Fig. 10.

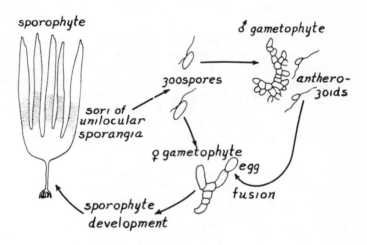

Fig. 10.   Diagram of the Life Cycle of *Laminaria*.

Although in the order Fucales, which contains many of our commonest rock weeds such as *Fucus, Pelvetia, Ascophyllum,* etc., the macroscopic plant of the field is the sporophyte generation, the life cycle differs markedly from that of *Laminaria* in the elimination of the gametophyte generation. The life cycle of *Fucus* is diagrammed in Fig. 11. Note that the number of functional eggs in the macrosporangium is a key character which is used in step 166 of the key.

Nothing has been said about the orders Ectocarpales and Dictyotales in which the gametophyte plants are present and are usually essentially like the sporophyte plants. At this point the student need only be aware that he will encounter both asexual and sexual plants of these groups in his collecting and that in most cases either will serve equally well with regard to the use of this illustrated key.

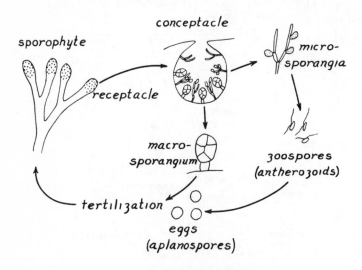

Fig. 11. Diagram of the Life Cycle of *Fucus*.

THE RED ALGAE

The elementary student of phycology has long been perplexed by the problem of recognition of various kinds of red algae in the field, for many of them are not really red in color, but green, brown, purple or even blackish in nature. He is further discouraged when told that their primary morphological distinction from other algae is found in the presence of non-motile male gametes which fuse with a special female sex organ, the carpogonium. It is because of such situations which often make it practically impossible for a beginning student to place his specimens in the right algal division that the present artificial key is designed to key out all groups together without regard to natural relationships.

Nevertheless, in the use of the key one will find frequent cause to be acquainted with some of the fundamental aspects of reproduction in the Red Algae, for in this group especially, the reproductive structures are often conspicuous and serve conveniently in the recognition of a number of **genera**.

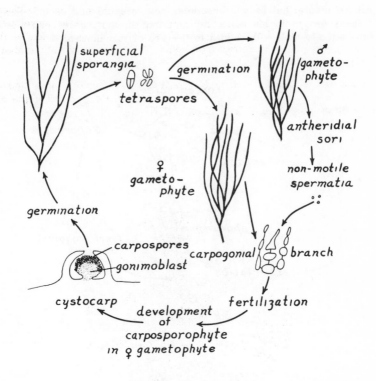

Fig. 12. Diagram of the life cycle of *Gracilaria*.

Again as a broad generalization it may be said that a large majority of the Red Algae have an alternation of not two, but three generations, namely a sporophyte and a gametophyte generation which are isomorphic, and a carposporophyte generation which remains attached to and, in a sense, parasitic on the gametophyte generation. Briefly, a macroscopic sporophyte plant produces non-motile asexual spores, usually tetraspores, which germinate to produce separate male and female gametophyte plants. The male plants produce non-motile sexual cells (spermatia) which are freed and lodge against and fuse with the female sex organ (carpogonium) on the female plant. As a result of gametic union which may occur in a variety of ways, a new generation begins development in or on the female gametophyte. This

24

generation consists of a tissue called a gonimoblast which produces carpospores in a number of ways, often within a special enveloping structure called the cystocarp (See Figs. 38-39). The liberation of the carpospores and their germination begins the development of the sporophyte generation again, whereby the cycle is repeated.

The genus *Gracilaria* may be used as an example of this kind of life cycle (Fig. 12) which is characteristic of most of the red algae except those of the orders Bangiales and Nemalionales.

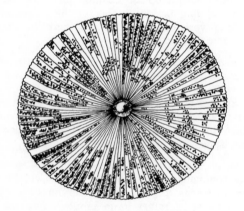

USE OF THE PICTURED-KEY

THE success with which the following key may be used will depend firstly, upon the adequacy of the specimens for identification, secondly, upon the care with which they are examined, and thirdly, upon the accuracy with which terms in the key are interpreted. A microscope is a prerequisite in this study, for many of the marine algae can be identified only by observing certain features of reproduction or of internal anatomy. However, in the present key an attempt has been made to simplify the identification process so that, for the most part, only relatively gross microscopical examinations are required. Indeed, the student will find that a number of the larger algae, especially those bearing vesicles, veins or ribs, may be identified entirely on macroscopic characters.

It cannot be overemphasized that the specimen must be adequate before identification is attempted, for a juvenile, sterile, or fragmentary algal specimen will often present the same difficulties with respect to the use of a key as does a flowering plant for which only a leaf or a piece of root has been collected. As more and more field experience is gained by the student, the problems of recognizing and selecting suitable specimens will diminish.

The key treats of marine algae such as may be encountered on any coast of the continental United States, and it will be noted that in a good many instances a genus will occur on both Atlantic and Pacific coasts. However, a rather large proportion of the algae are relatively localized, and for this reason an indication of the geographic distribution is given in each case.

Of necessity, for lack of space, only the larger and commoner marine algae are treated here, and in the majority of cases only as to genus, although the full specific name is provided for most of the habit illustrations. Thus, the student must be aware that some of the genera of plants he collects in any given area may not be illustrated in this brief account.

It should be pointed out here that the sequence in which the genera appear in the key is entirely artificial and bears no necessary connection with phylogenetic relationships. However, in order that the student may orient himself as to the relationships of the various plants, each is numbered in the index according to an appended list in which they appear in the phylogenetic sequence ordinarily encountered in the more modern taxonomic treatises.

ADDITIONAL REFERENCES

S the examination and identification of specimens progresses the student will find it desirable to supplement the information found herein by using local floristic accounts of the algae of his particular region. There are several of these which are well illustrated and will be useful, although by no means all of the coastal areas of the United States are covered in detail. Unfortunately, none of them contain a single comprehensive key to the genera which they treat, and so will be most helpful in the making of specific identifications after the genus has been determined by means of the present book. It is also in these special floristic accounts or in the literature to which they provide references that the smaller, rarer, localized and (or) less conspicuous plants may be sought.

Dawson, E. Y. 1945. An annotated list of the marine algae and marine grasses of San Diego County, California Occas. Papers San Diego Soc. Nat. Hist. (7): 1-87.

————— 1961. A guide to the literature and distributions of Pacific benthic algae from Alaska to the Galapagos Islands. Pacific Science 15(3): 370-461.

Doty, M. S. 1947. The marine algae of Oregon, I-II. Farlowia 3: 1-65, 159-215, 14 pls.

Hoyt, W. D. 1920. Marine algae of Beaufort, N. C., and adjacent regions. Bull. Bureau of Fisheries 36: 368-556, pls. 84-119.

Kylin, H. 1925. The marine red algae in the vicinity of the biological station at Friday Harbor, Wash. Lunds Univ. Arsskr., N.F., 21(9): 1-87. 47 figs.

Setchell, W. A. and N. L. Gardner 1920. The marine algae of the Pacific Coast of North America. Part 2, Chlorophyceae. Univ. Calif. Pub. Bot. 8: 139-381. 25 pls.

————— 1925. The marine algae of the Pacific Coast of North America. Part 3, Melanophyceae. Ibid. 8: 383-898. 20 pls.

Smith, G. M. 1944. Marine algae of the Monterey Peninsula, California. ix + 622 pp., 98 pls. Stanford Univ. Press.

Taylor, W. R. 1960. Marine algae of the eastern tropical and subtropical coasts of the Americas. xii + 870 pp. Univ. Michigan Press.

————— 1937. Marine algae of the northeastern coast of North America. i-vii + 427 pp., 60 pls. Univ. Michigan Press, Ann Arbor.

PICTURED-KEY TO THE COMMON GENERA OF MACROSCOPIC MARINE ALGAE OF THE UNITED STATES

1a Thallus consisting of a single large, subspherical cell with basal attachment. Fig. 13..124

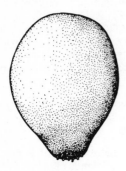

Fig. 13. *Valonia ventricosa* J. Agardh

An entire plant showing the single large spherical cell with basal rhizoids for attachment, × 1.5.

Figure 13

1b Thallus consisting of more than one cell, or if coenocytic, at least not subspherical in form......................................2

2a Thallus more or less calcareous, the calcium carbonate deposited superficially in the outer tissues, in articulated segments, or throughout the entire thallus......................................106
(If in doubt about the calcareous nature apply a little dilute acid to a *clean* piece of thallus and watch for bubbles under a dissecting microscope.)

2b Thallus not calcareous.......................................3

3a Entire thallus hollow, subglobular to tubular, or the thallus with hollow, septate or unseptate branches, or provided with hollow bladders, bulbs or vesicles. Fig. 14 82

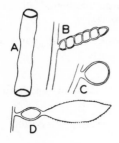

Figure 14

Fig. 14. Several examples of hollow structures in the algae.

A. A hollow tubular thallus as in *Enteromorpha*. B. A hollow branch provided with septation or diaphragms as in *Gastroclonium*. C. A solitary, hollow vesicle as in *Botryocladia*. D. A hollow vesicle (pneumatocyst) at the base of a vegetative blade as in *Macrocystis*.

3b Thallus without hollow structures or parts (except sometimes the coarse stipe, as in *Postelsia*) 4

4a Thallus crustose, forming a thin, adherent expanse on the substrate, or, prostrate and coarsely net-like 78

4b Thallus not crustose or net-like, free except for one or more basal attachments 5

5a Thallus consisting of one or more branched or unbranched uniseriate filaments Fig. 15, or consisting of a variously branched, free, essentially cylindrical filament without cellular septations (coenocytic) (See Figs. 89-92) 58

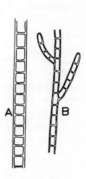

Figure 15

Fig. 15. Two forms of uniseriate filaments. A. An unbranched uniseriate filament as in *Chaetomorpha*. B. A branched uniseriate filament as in *Callithamnion*.

5b Thallus of various form and structure, but consisting neither of one or more branched or unbranched uniseriate filaments, nor of a branched, free, essentially cylindrical filament without cellular septations. (Note that some young stages, such as in *Bangia*, may be uniseriate; some *Caulerpa* species are coenocytic but not cylindrical; *Codium* is coenocytic but consists of interwined filaments whose only free parts are the external utricles).................6

6a Thallus membranous, only 1-2 cells thick, at least at the margins. Fig. 16 52

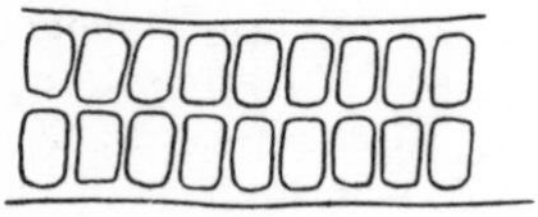

Fig. 16. A cross section of a distromatic thallus (2 cells thick) as .occurs in *Ulva*.

Figure 16

6b Thallus cylindrical or flattened; if membranous, with more than two layers of cells at the margins............................7

7a Vegetative portions of thallus dominantly compressed, flattened, or complanate. Fig. 17...125

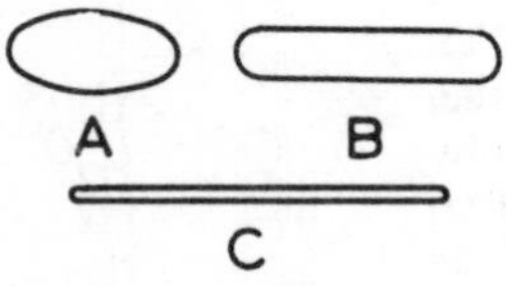

Fig. 17. Cross sectional forms of (A.) compressed, (B.) flattened, and (C.) complanate thalli.

A   B
C

Figure 17

7b Vegetative portions of thallus dominantly of cylindrical form, or, if compressed, only slightly so or only in restricted areas such as the points of branching...8

8a Growing apices showing a single apical cell, although this sometimes sunken in an apical pit (*Chondria, Laurencia*) or obscured
by terminal branchlets (especially *Dasya, Digenia, Wrangelia*) Fig.
18 26

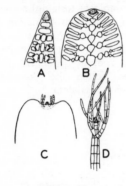

Figure 18

Fig. 18. Examples of apical cells.

A. As found on an acute apex. B. As
found on a blunt apex such as *Gelidium*
(seen in longitudinal section). C. Sunken
in an apical pit as in *Laurencia*. D. Somewhat obscured by terminal branchlets (or
trichoblasts or hairs) as in *Polysiphonia*.

In making observations of apical cells
one will usually have the best results
with young, actively growing vegetative
branch-tips rather than old or fertile ones.
In those plants in which the apex is obscured by enveloping branchlets it may
be necessary to dissect away the very
tip of a young branch and to crush it
under the cover slip on a slide in order to force the surrounding branchlets away and to make the apical cell area visible.

8b. Growing apices without a single apical cell from which growth
takes place 9

9a Growth trichothallic. Fig. 19................................. 24

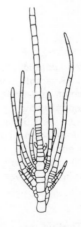

Figure 19

Fig. 19. An example of trichothallic growth
by means of a terminal hair with cell division at its base, as seen in the apex of
Haplogloia andersonii, × 300. Note that
the trichothallic type of growth will be difficult to interpret in *Heterochordaria abietina* (See Fig. 42). Its distinctive habit should
be recognized.

31

9b Growth apical (terminal) or intercalary, but not trichothallic. Fig. 20 10

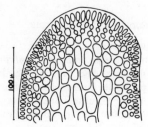

Fig. 20. An example of terminal growth by means of an apical meristem in which there is no evidence of a single apical cell, as seen in a longitudinal section of the apex of *Gracilaria*. This is sometimes called the "fountain type" of apical meristem.

Figure 20

10a Thallus a simple, unbranched filament 250 μ in diameter or less, with intercalary growth, at first uniseriate Fig. 21, later becoming multiseriate ....*Bangia*

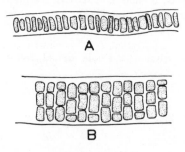

A

B

Figure 21

Fig. 21. *Bangia fuscopurpurea* (Dillwyn) Lyngbye
   A. A small portion of a young filament showing the uniseriate character and flattened shape of the cells, $\times$ 190. B. An older part of a filament showing the multiseriate condition, $\times$ 190. Growth is by intercalary cell division. This delicate but often abundant and conspicuous plant occurs both on the Atlantic and Pacific coasts as a slippery, hairy covering on rocks and woodwork, the filaments sometimes reaching 20 cm. in length. Several other minute epiphytic species of this genus may be encountered.

10b Thallus more than 500 μ in diameter, branched or unbranched..11

11a Thallus usually of firm consistency, of more or less parenchymatous type structure, at least in the cortical and outer medullary regions. Fig. 22. 18

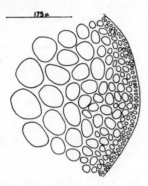

Fig. 22. Part of a transverse section of *Gracilaria* to show the parenchymatous type, large, relatively thin-walled, more or less isodiametrical cells of the medulla. In this instance there is a gradual transition from the largest medullary cells to the small cells of the cortex.

Figure 22

11b Thallus not of parenchymatous type structure, soft or firm. 12

12a Thallus wiry, rigid, cartilaginous, the medulla of densely packed longitudinal filaments, the cortex of dense anticlinal cell rows. Fig. 23. . . . .*Ahnfeltia*

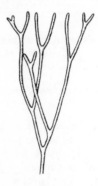

Fig. 23. *Ahnfeltia plicata* (Hudson) Fries

A small portion of a plant to show the cylindrical, regularly dichotomous branches, × 1.5. This species occurs both in New England and along the Pacific Coast. *A. concinna* J. Agardh is a coarser species of greater diameter which is found occasionally along the Pacific Coast.

Figure 23

12b Thallus soft, spongy, or often gelatinous, (firm in *Chordaria*), consisting of variously branched, interlaced or intertwined filaments which may be more or less compacted in the medulla but are externally free. 13

13a Thallus filaments without cross walls, ending at the surface in a continuous layer of inflated utricles. Fig. 24 . . . . *Codium*

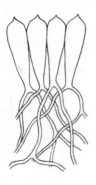

Figure 24

Fig. 24. *Codium fragile* (Suringar) Hariot

A small group of utricles showing their origin from the non-septate, branched filaments making up the thallus, × 50. In this species the utricles are pointed, but in other species they are smooth. Several kinds of *Codium* occur along the Pacific Coast and along the Atlantic Coast from North Carolina southward. The commonest Atlantic species, *C. dichotomum* (Hudson) S. F. Gray and the common Pacific one, *C. fragile*, are both erect, dichotomously branched, cylindrical plants. Other species are flattened at the points of branching while still others are prostrate and somewhat cushion-shaped or with lobe-like branches.

13b Thallus filaments with cross walls; surface without inflated utricles 14

14a Brownish in color; axis with a solid medulla of compacted, branched, longitudinal filaments 15

14b Reddish in color; medullary region not solid, the thallus filaments nowhere compacted 16

15a Thallus gelatinous; branching irregular; ultimate branches often short. Fig. 25 . . . . *Eudesme virescens*

Fig. 25. *Eudesme virescens* (Carmichael) J. Agardh

A small upper portion of a plant to show the irregular short branches and the compacted medulla which shows through the looser, more gelatinous cortical region as a denser core, × 1.5. This species is found widely along the Atlantic Coast. It is the only member of the genus in our flora. A slender form commonly grows on the leaves of *Zostera*.

Figure 25

15b Thallus firm; branching regular; ultimate branches long. Fig. 26
....*Chordaria*

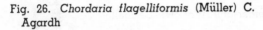

Fig. 26. *Chordaria flagelliformis* (Müller) C. Agardh

A small upper portion of a plant about 40 cm. long showing the smooth, slender, long branches, × 0.6. Found on the New England coast. *C. dissessa* Setchell & Gardner, a species of somewhat irregular diameter and flattening at the points of branching, occurs in the Puget Sound area of Washington.

Figure 26

16a Thallus simple, or furcately branched. Fig. 27.
....................................*Nemalion*

Fig. 27. *Nemalion helminthoides* (Velley) Batters

An entire plant, × 0.6. Frequent on rocks at rather high intertidal levels along the Pacific Coast. A similar but more abundantly branched species occurs on exposed rocks along the New England coast and is known as *N. multifidum* (Weber & Mohr) J. Agardh.

Figure 27

17a Thallus of several long axes bearing numerous short, mostly simple lateral branchlets. Fig. 28..............*Cumagloia andersonii*

Fig. 28. *Cumagloia andersonii* (Farlow) Setchell & Gardner

An entire plant, $\times$ 0.6. On rocks at high intertidal levels along the Pacific Coast.

Figure 28

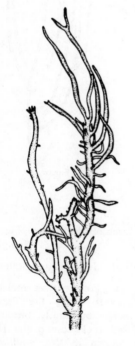

17b Thallus irregularly and indeterminately branched in 1-3 orders. Fig. 29. ....*Helminthocladia californica*

Fig. 29. *Helminthocladia californica* (J. Agardh) Kylin

The upper part of a plant $\times$ 0.6. Occasional in upper intertidal pools along southern California.

Figure 29

18a Thallus solid and smooth, the cortex without a conspicuous superficial layer of hairs and paraphyses..........................20

18b Cortex bearing conspicuous superficial hairs, filaments, or paraphyses. Fig. 30..19

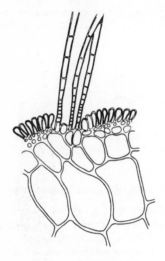

Fig. 30. *Chorda filum* (Linnaeus) Lamouroux

Part of a transaction of a thallus to show the parenchymatous structure and the presence of conspicuous superficial hairs. For habit and other comments see Figure 32.

Figure 30

19a Thallus subdichotomously branched; cortex bearing arcuate filaments in clumps. Fig. 31....................*Stilophora rhizoides*

Fig. 31. *Stilophora rhizoides* (Ehrhart) J. Agardh

The upper part of a plant to show the rough surface due to clumps of hairs, and the loose, remote branches, × 1.2. This is the only species of the genus on our coasts. It occurs in quiet bays from North Carolina northward to New England.

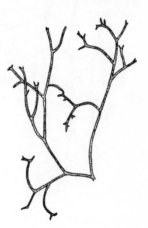

Figure 31

37

19b Thallus whip-like, essentially unbranched; cortical hairs and paraphyses not in clumps. Fig. 30, 32...............*Chorda* (in part)

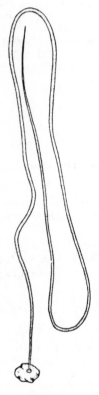

Fig. 32. *Chorda filum* (Linnaeus) Lamouroux

An entire plant, $\times$ 0.3, showing the unbranched, whip-like form. Young, growing plants
will show, when held in water, an outer covering of delicate, colorless hairs which fall away
with age. The terminal parts of old plants are
usually partly decayed. This species which is
widespread on both sides of the north Atlantic
occurs commonly near low tide level and below from New Jersey northward, usually attached in groups on stones or shells. Another
species, *C. tomentosum* Lyngbye, is more densely covered with hairs and occurs north of Cape
Cod. Some adult forms of *Chorda* are more
or less hollow and will key out best under step
91b.

Figure 32

20a Medulla containing slender, more or less longitudinal filaments aggregated in the center of a parenchymatous tissue. Fig. 33...21

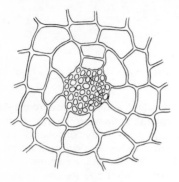

Figure 33

Fig. 33. *Agardhiella coulteri* (Harvey) Setchell

The inner medullary part of the thallus as seen in cross section showing the large, thin-walled, parenchymatous cells surrounding the central core of slender, elongated, relatively thick-walled filamentous cells.

20b Medulla entirely of more or less isodiametrical cells. (See Fig. 22) 22

21a Branches relatively slender, narrow at the base and gradually tapering to the apex. Figs. 33, 34....................*Agardhiella*

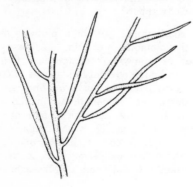

Figure 34

Fig. 34. *Agardhiella tenera* (J. Agardh) Schmitz

A small mid-portion of a plant, × 1.4. This species is abundant below low water level along the Atlantic Coast south of Cape Cod and along the Gulf of Mexico. Another species of more robust habit, *A. coulteri* (Harvey) Setchell, occurs along the entire Pacific Coast.

**21b Branches thick, not narrowed at the base, not attenuated. Fig.
35**...*Eucheuma* (in part)

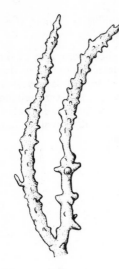

Fig. 35. *Eucheuma isiforme* (C. Agardh)
J. Agardh

Part of a plant such as may reach 30-
50 cm. in height, showing coarse, succulent branches and warty surface, × 0.7.
This and other subcylindrical species may
be found in Florida and westward along
the Gulf coast. Other species are flattened
but are of infrequent occurence.

Figure 35

**22a Branching dichotomous, at least in part, and mainly in one plane.
Fig. 36**...............................*Gymnogongrus griffithsiae*

Fig. 36. *Gymnogongrus griffithsiae* (Turner) Martius

A small upper part of a plant to show
the dichotomous branching of the cylindrical or somewhat compressed thallus,
× 2. Although several flat species of *Gymnogongrus* occur in our flora and will be
accounted for farther along in the key
this is the only cylindrical one on our
coasts. The densely bushy little plants
reach about 5 cm. in height and grow
just below low water mark along the entire Atlantic Coast south of Massachusetts.

Figure 36

22b Branching not dichotomous, but multifarious. Fig. 37.........23

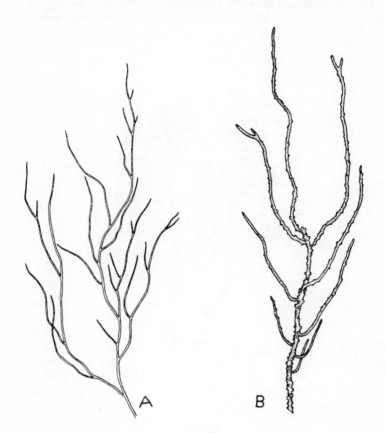

Figure 37

Fig. 37. Branching habit of *Gracilariopsis*

A. Part of a sterile plant of a *Gracilariopsis* species to show the irregular, multifarious branching of the slender, cylindrical thallus, × 1. B. Part of a fertile, cystocarpic plant of *Gracilariopsis sjoestedtii* (Kylin) Dawson showing the cylindrical form, the protruding, subhemispherical cystocarps, and the irregular, multifarious branching. See also comments at Fig. 39.

23a Gonimoblast placenta of relatively large, vacuolate cells and with
nutritive filaments extending into the pericarp. Fig. 38..........
.... *Gracilaria verrucosa*

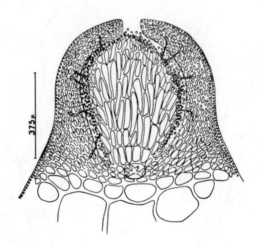

Figure 38

Fig. 38. *Gracilaria* sp.

A vertical section through a cystocarp showing the large-celled
central gonimoblast placenta from which nutritive filaments extend
out into the wall of the cystocarp (pericarp). The opening at the top
of the cystocarp is the ostiole. Carpospores are seen being produced
from the outer cells of the gonimoblast. Most of the species of *Gracilaria* are more or less flattened (See Fig. 233) but one common cylindrical
one is *G. verrucosa* (Greville) Papenfuss which may be found both along
the Atlantic and Pacific coasts. It has been exploited commercially
as a source of agar although the product obtained is of a lower
quality than that obtained from species of *Gelidium*.

23b Gonimoblast placenta of small cells, without nutritive filaments
extending into the pericarp. Fig. 39...............*Gracilariopsis*

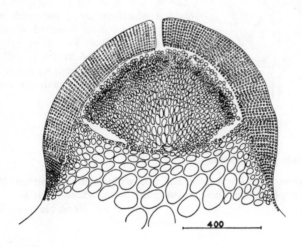

Figure 39

Fig. 39. *Gracilariopsis sjoestedtii* (Kylin) Dawson

A vertical section through a mature cystocarp showing the small-
celled, dense gonimoblast placenta and the absence of nutritive filaments connecting with the pericarp. This species occurs along the
Pacific Coast from central Oregon southward and has been identified from North Carolina and Florida by the writer. It should be
pointed out that this plant and *Gracilaria verrucosa* are indistinguish-
able except with regard to the cystocarps and antheridia which in
the former are superficial and in the latter are produced in deep
pocket-like cavities. One other species of *Gracilariopsis* occurs commonly along the southern California coast, *G. andersonii* (Grunow)
Dawson. It is relatively short and tufted.

24a Branching pinnate and opposite. Fig. 40.....*Desmarestia* (in part)

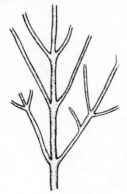

Fig. 40. *Desmarestia viridis* (Müller) Lamouroux

A small portion of a plant to show the opposite branching of the slender, cylindrical axes. Most of the species of *Desmarestia* are flattened or complanate, but this one which occurs to the north of New Jersey, and is also reported from California, is cylindrical. Two other cylindrical species (*D. media* (Agardh) Greville and *D. farcta* Setchell & Gardner) occur in the Puget Sound area of Washington, usually in infratidal habitats.

Figure 40

24b Branching not pinnate.......................................25

25a Branches all of irregular lengths, without the formation of very distinct percurrent axes in the plant as a whole. Fig. 41........ ....*Haplogloia andersonii*

Fig. 41. *Haplogloia andersonii* (Farlow) Levring

A small portion of the upper part of a plant, $\times$ 1.5, to show the irregular multifarious branching and the dense covering of fine hairs over the whole surface of the thallus. The structure of the growing apex of this plant is shown in Fig. 19. Occasional at low tide levels along the entire Pacific Coast. In the middle parts of its range it is known to begin its development late in the winter and to mature and disappear again by the beginning of summer.

Figure 41

25b Thallus with more or less uniform, short, multifarious branchlets borne on percurrent axes. Fig. 42.......*Heterochordaria abietina*

Fig. 42. *Heterochordaria abietina* (Ruprecht) Setchell & Gardner

Part of a group of erect axes, × 1. A common species at middle tide levels from central California northward to Alaska. Plants reach 20-25 cm. in height. The axes and branches, which at first are solid, may later become hollow but usually will not give the impression of being hollow unless sectioned.

Figure 42

26a Thallus more or less corticated, but ultimate branchlets either
    strictly uniseriate or corticated only by bands. Fig. 43........27

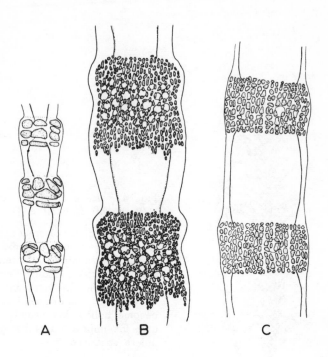

Figure 43

Fig. 43. Examples of small portions of three different *Ceramium* spe-
    cies, (A. × 250; B-C. × 100) to show various kinds of cortical
    bands encircling the relatively very large cells of the uniseriate
    axes.

26b Ultimate branchlets neither uniseriate nor incompletely corticated
    by cortical bands, but completely corticated and (or) with many
    rows or layers of cells....................................32

27a Ultimate branchlets uniseriate but with cortical bands........28

27b Ultimate branchlets strictly uniseriate, without cortical bands...29

28a Axes completely corticated, unlike the ultimate branchlets which are uniseriate except for cortical bands. Fig. 44 . . . . *Spyridia*

Figure 44

Fig. 44. *Spyridia filamentosa* (Wulfen) Harvey

A small part of a completely corticated axis and part of two banded ultimate branchlets, × 80. This delicately bushy little plant occurs widely along the Atlantic coast and in southernmost California. It is essentially a tropical species which inhabits protected, warm bays and pools in the northern parts of its range. Another species, bearing spines on the upper nodes, occurs in Florida (*S. aculeata* (Schimper) Kützing).

28b Axes and branches all similar, banded. Fig. 45 . . . .
. . . . *Ceramium* (in part)

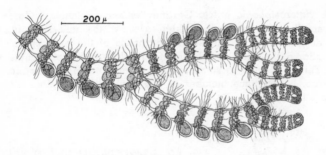

200 μ

Figure 45

Fig. 45. *Ceramium avalonae* Dawson

A small part of a plant to show the cortical bands, the caliper-like tips characteristic of several species, and one manner of production of tetrasporangia. The very fine lateral hairs are also present on a number of species. *C. avalonae* occurs in southern California.

The genus *Ceramium* is a large one containing many incompletely corticated as well as completely corticated species (See Figs. 43, 61). The incompletely corticated ones are usually quite small species of warm waters, while the heavily corticated ones are usually larger and of more temperate distribution. Specific identifications in the genus must be made through the use of the more comprehensive floristic works. The writer has presented an illustrated analysis of the twenty-nine species occurring on the Pacific Coast of North America in Farlowia, vol. 4, pp. 113-138.

29a Thallus showing a gradation from a multiseriate (polysiphonous) condition to a uniseriate condition in the ultimate ranks of branches. Figs. 46, 47......................................*Heterosiphonia*

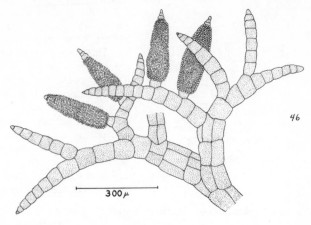

Figure 46

Fig. 46. *Heterosiphonia erecta* Gardner, emend. Setchell & Gardner

A small upper part of a plant to show the uniseriate ultimate branchlets arising from multiseriate branches of the prior order. Note the peculiar antheridial branchlets on this plant with their minute spermatia. This is a common small species along southern California. The only large, conspicuous member of this genus in the United States is *H. gibbesii* (Fig. 47).

Fig. 47. *Heterosiphonia gibbesii* (Harvey) Falkenberg

A small upper portion of a plant, $\times$ 1.25. This is the largest species of the genus in our flora, occurring in Florida and reaching 10-20 cm. in height.

Figure 47

48

29b Thallus without such a gradation from a multiseriate to a uniseriate condition in the ultimate ranks of branches. Fig. 48........30

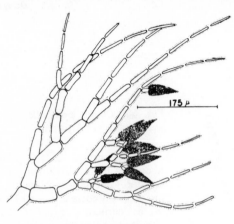

Fig. 48. *Dasya* sp.

A single lateral branch as separated from the corticated main axis showing several ranks of uniseriate branchlets, and several conical antheridial branchlets. These uniseriate branchlets are here much magnified, and to the naked eye appear as very fine hairs both in *Dasya* and in *Wrangelia*.

Figure 48

30a Main axes corticated (at least to some extent in lower parts) by means of the growth of filaments from cells at the nodes, Fig. 49; branchlets arising only at points of junction of axial cells......31

Fig. 49. *Callithamnion* sp.

A small piece of a plant showing branching from two nodes and an early stage in development of cortication by growth of descending filaments from the nodal cells. × 85.

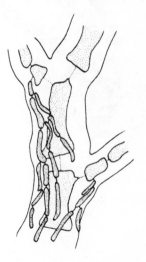

Figure 49

49

30b Main axes corticated just back of apices, not by filaments from the nodes; uniseriate branchlets arising from all parts of the cortical surface. Fig. 50...*Dasya*

Fig. 50. *Dasya pedicellata* (C. Agardh) C. Agardh

A mid-portion of a plant about 15 cm. high showing the slender lateral branchlets arising from all parts of the surface of the corticated axis, × 1.2. The dark bodies represent cystocarps. Although a single Pacific Coast species, *Dasya pacifica* Gardner, occurs abundantly at La Jolla, California during the summer, this genus is otherwise restricted in the United States to the Atlantic Coast. *D. pedicellata* is the common species there, occurring all the way from Texas through Florida to Massachusetts. It is usually found in protected waters at depths of 3 to 12 feet below low water level. There are several other species known from Florida, but they are of infrequent or rare occurrence.

Figure 50

50

31a Major branching mostly 2-ranked; ultimate branchlets more or
less verticillate. Fig. 51..............................*Wrangelia*

Figure 51

Fig. 51. *Wrangelia penicillata*
C. Agardh

A small upper part of a plant
to show the branching in two
ranks and the tufted and somewhat verticillate manner of production of the ultimate branchlets, × 5. This is the largest
of three species found in Florida. It may reach a size of
10-20 centimeters.

31b Major branching distichous or multifarious; no order of branching
verticillate. Fig. 52........*Callithamnion* (in part); also *Seirospora*

Callithamnion is a rather large genus of quite delicate, often small
plants which may be either epiphytic or saxicolous and which may be
found along almost any part of our coasts. Some of them are completely without cortication and will be treated elsewhere in this key
(step 76b). Several other species are corticated only in lower parts,
while *C. pikeanum* is corticated almost to the apex. In all of them the
alternate arrangement of the uniseriate branchlets of the last orders
and the tetrahedrally divided sporangia are characteristic (See Fig.
108).

There is one plant of another genus which has these characters
and which will key out here. This is the Atlantic coastal *Seirospora
griffithsiana* Harvey (Fig. 53) which, however, is readily recognized by
its seirospores which are produced abundantly during the summer
in addition to the usual tetraspores.

Figure 52

Fig. 52. *Callithamnion pikeanum* Harvey

A portion of an axis with a single primary lateral branch, × 1. This is the coarsest of our *Callithamnion* species and the only one with such heavy cortication. It occurs commonly on rocks at middle intertidal levels along the whole Pacific Coast except southernmost California.

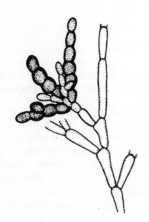

Figure 53

Fig. 53. *Seirospora griffithsiana* Harvey

A small upper portion of a plant bearing seirospores, × 150. Epiphytic on *Zostera* and various algae from New Jersey to Cape Cod.

52

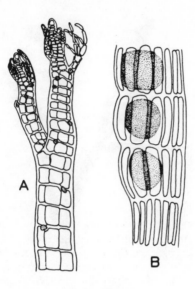

Figure 54

Fig. 54. Appearances of pericentral cells in two different plants.

A. The apex of a *Polysiphonia* species showing short pericentral cells, scar-cells, trichoblasts and apical cells, × 100. B. A short piece of a *Lophosiphonia* species with a large number of long pericentral cells surrounding developing tetrasporangia, × 150. *Lophosiphonia* is a small, inconspicuous plant not treated in the key.

33a Cylindrical axes more or less densely clothed with slender, bristle-like lateral branchlets. Fig. 55...................*Digenia simplex*

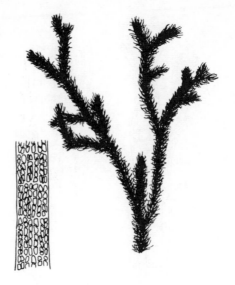

Figure 55

Fig. 55. *Digenia simplex* (Wulfen) C. Agardh

A. An upper part of a plant of rather lax habit, $\times$ 0.8. B. A small part of a single lateral, determinate branchlet to show the cortication, $\times$ 80. Although it is difficult to observe the apical cell of main axes because of the abundant lateral branchlets, the apical cells of the determinate laterals are often readily observed. This is a common tropical plant of Florida and the Gulf of Mexico to Texas. Under favorable conditions when the water is well protected the plants may become luxuriantly developed and much-branched, up to 8 to 10 inches high, while in rough, surfy localities the plants are usually stubby, dwarfish and little-branched. They are commonly of unsightly appearance because of multitudes of epiphytes which cover them.

33b Axes not clothed with slender, hair-like lateral branchlets (but note also *Odonthalia floccosa*, step 179)......................34

34a Growing point sunken in an apical pit, Fig. 56, and surrounded
   (at least when actively growing) by long or short hairs. (See Fig.
   18c) 37

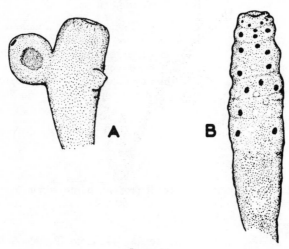

Figure 56

Fig. 56. *Laurencia* sp.

A cystocarpic branchlet (A.), and a tetrasporic branchlet (B.) to
show apical pit of mature branchlets after the hairs, which originally
surround the apical cell, have fallen away, $\times$ 23.

34b Growing point not sunken in an apical pit......................35

35a Thallus showing a single axial filament of very large cells covered by a thin cortex of much smaller cells. Fig. 57..........36

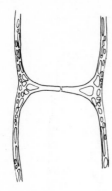

Fig. 57. *Ceramium* sp.

A longitudinal section through a node to show two of the large central axial cells and the thin cortex of small cells covering them, × 65. This structural feature usually may be discerned by obtaining a median optical focus with the microscope using strong light.

Figure 57

35b Axial filament not as above; if present, borne within a medullary tissue. Fig. 58...38

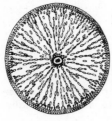

Fig. 58. *Endocladia muricata* (Postels & Ruprecht) J. Agardh

A cross section of a branch to show the conspicuous large axial filament and the radiating medullary filaments, × 50.

Figure 58

36a Cortical cells in regular vertical rows; axes bearing whorls of 2-celled spines at regular intervals. Fig. 59..*Centroceras clavulatum*

Fig. 59. *Centroceras clavulatum (C. Agardh) Montagne*

A small part of a branch to show the regular arrangement of the cortical cells and the whorls of spines × 120. A common small plant of Florida, the Gulf of Mexico and southern California, often mixed with other small algae in tufts.

Figure 59

36b Cortical cells not in regular rows; axes without whorls of 2-celled spines. Figs. 60, 61..........................*Ceramium* (in part)

Fig. 60. *Ceramium pacificum* (Collins) Kylin

A very small part of a branch to show the irregular arrangement of the cortical cells over the large, subspherical cells of the axial filament, × 190. A widely distributed species from southern California to Vancouver Island.

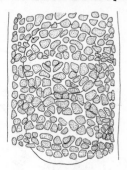

Figure 60

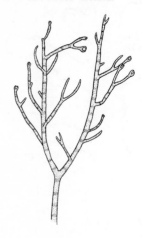

Figure 61

Fig. 61. *Ceramium rubrum* (Hudson) C. Agardh

A small upper part of a plant, × 6. This is the largest and commonest of the completely corticated *Ceramium* species of the Atlantic Coast, occurring from Florida to Newfoundland. On the Pacific Coast *C. pacificum* (Collins) Kylin and *C. eatonianum* (Farlow) De Toni are similar, while *C. codicola* J. Agardh is a common epiphyte on *Codium*. For other, incompletely corticated *Ceramium* species see step 28b and Figs. 43, 45.

Figure 62

37a Branchlets contracted at the base, 500 μ or less in diameter. Fig. 62......
....................*Chondria* (in part)

Fig. 62. *Chondria sedifolia* Harvey

A small upper part of a tetrasporic plant, × 4. This is the only one of our common *Chondria* species with depressed apices. Plants reach 10-15 cm. in height and occur along the whole Atlantic Coast to as far north as Massachusetts.

37b Branchlets mostly not contracted at the base, 750 μ or more in diameter. Figs. 63, 64........................*Laurencia* (in part)

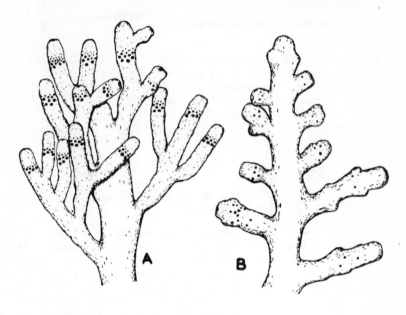

Figure 63

Fig. 63. *Laurencia* spp. (tetrasporangial branch apices)

Two examples of upper branches of tetrasporangial plants to show the slight contraction at the base of branches compared to the prominent contraction in *Chondria*. A. × 5; B. × 9.

Fig. 64. *Laurencia* spp. (habit)

A. *Laurencia papillosa* (Forskal) Greville. Habit of a portion of a clumping plant, × 1.5. B. *Laurencia obtusa* (Hudson) Lamouroux. Habit of a portion of a clumping plant, × 1.5. Both of these species are common along the coasts of Florida and the Gulf of Mexico. Several other cylindrical species occur more or less commonly in Florida and also along the California coast where *L. pacifica* Kylin is the most wide-spread and abundant one. Flattened species of *Laurencia* key out under step 181a (See Fig. 226).

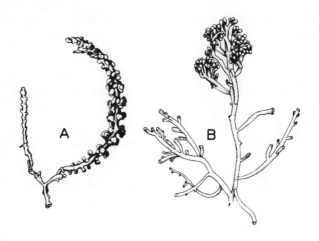

Figure 64

38a Thallus gelatinous and slippery; cortex of short, free filaments with large terminal cells. Fig. 65.............*Sphaerotrichia divaricata*

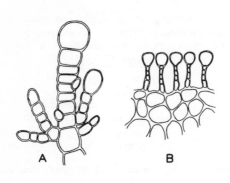

Figure 65

Fig. 65. *Sphaerotrichia divaricata* (C. Agardh) Kylin

A. The apex of a plant highly magnified to show the enlarged apical cell, × 560. B. A small portion of a transection of a thallus to show the free cortical filaments with their large terminal cells, × 200. The structural features .of this plant and other such gelatinous forms are usually best observed by crushing out terminal portions of branches on a slide. Commonly epiphytic on larger algae during the summer from New Jersey northward. Some forms tend to be hollow.

38b Thallus not particularly gelatinous or slippery; cortex not as above 39

39a Medulla of filaments radiating from the large, central axial filament. Figs. 58, 66 .... *Endocladia muricata*

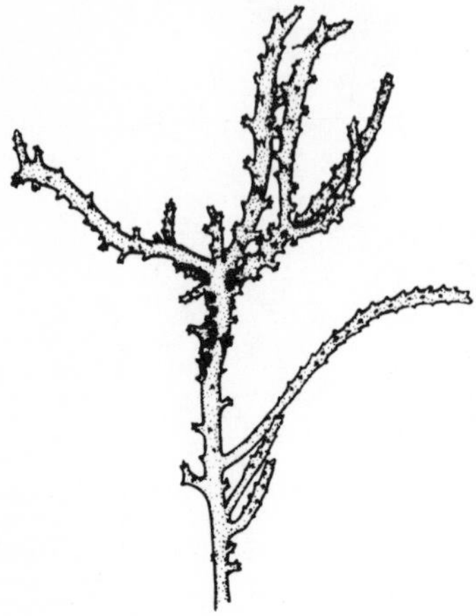

Fig. 66. *Endocladia muricata* (Postels & Ruprecht) J. Agardh

A small portion of a clump to show the spiny character of the branches, × 5. A common, low, densely tufted or matted plant on rocks at rather high intertidal levels along the entire Pacific Coast.

Figure 66

39b Medulla more or less parenchymatous. Fig. 67 40

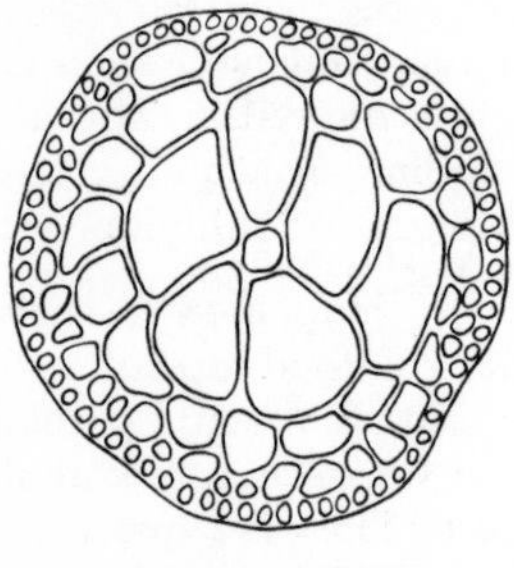

Fig. 67. *Hypnea* sp.

A transection of a thallus to show the parenchymatous type of structure, × 30. Habit drawings of various *Hypnea* species are shown in figures 68 and 71.

Figure 67

40a Thallus bearing occasional conspicuous sickle-shaped (hamate) structures 41

40b Thallus without sickle-shaped (hamate) parts 42

41a Hamate structures terminal on main branches; lateral branchlets relatively sparse, irregular in length. Fig. 68..*Hypnea musciformis*

Fig. 68. *Hypnea musciformis* (Wulfen) Lamouroux

A small upper part of a plant, × 1.5, showing the hamate branch tips and the irregular, unequal lateral branchlets. This tropical plant ranges northward to Massachusetts in warm, protected places. Other species of the genus lack hamate tips and key out at step 43b.

Figure 68

41b Hamate structures lateral on main branches; lateral branchlets relatively uniform in length. Fig. 69.............*Bonnemaisonia*

Fig. 69. *Bonnemaisonia hamifera* Hariot

A small part of a plant to show the lateral hamate branch and the relatively uniform slender, lateral branchlets, × 3.6. An occasional to common epiphyte in spring in southern New England and also in southern California. Another species, *B. nootkana* (Esper) Silva, occurs from central California northward.

Figure 69

42a Thallus bearing short, simple or compound spine-like branchlets **43**

42b Thallus smooth, without specialized spine-like branchlets......**44**

61

43a Short branchlets much reduced, compound but not forked or stellate. Fig. 70 . . . . *Acanthophora spicifera*

Fig. 70. *Acanthophora spicifera* (Vahl) Börgesen

A small portion of a densely branched form to show the compound, short spine-like branchlets, × 5. This widely distributed tropical species has been known in the Caribbean Sea since it was described in 1799 from the Virgin Islands. It is commonly encountered in infratidal waters of Florida. Another species occurs in the Florida keys, but is rare.

Figure 70

43b Short branchlets simple, forked or stellate. Fig. 71 . . . .
. . . .**Hypnea (in part)**

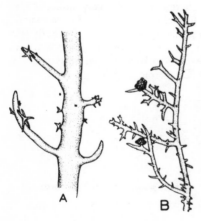

Fig. 71. *Hypnea* spp.

A. *Hypnea cornuta* (Lamouroux) J. Agardh. A small part of an axis magnified × 6.4 to show the stellate branchlets. B. *Hypnea cervicornis* J. Agardh. Habit of a small part of a matted plant showing shell fragments attached by small discs and simple, spine-like branchlets, × 2.4. Both of these are tropical plants of Florida and the Gulf Coast. Two or three other species may be encountered in this region as well as the distinctive *H. musciformis* which appears in the key at step 41a. Two other species are frequent in southern California during the summer.

A

B

Figure 71

44a Young growing points with short or long deciduous hairs around the apical cell. Fig. 72 . . . .*Chondria* (in part)

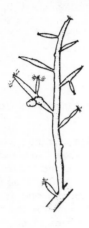

Fig. 72. *Chondria tenuissima* (Goodenough & Woodward) C. Agardh.

A small portion of a plant to show the branched, deciduous hairs aggregated around the growing apices and the spindle-shaped branches, $\times$ 5. This is the coarser of the two common species of *Chondria* with emergent apices along the Atlantic coast as far north as New England. Two other species occur north of New Jersey, several to the south of North Carolina, and two species are abundant in southern California. They vary from quite delicate plants with main axes less than ½ mm. thick to quite large, coarse plants 25 cm. tall with axes 2 mm. thick.

Figure 72

44b Young growing points without deciduous hairs especially aggregated around the apical cell. Fig. 18b **45**

45a Medulla, especially the outer medulla, with slender, rhizoidal filaments packed between the larger medullary cells. Figs. 73,74. . . . .*Gelidium* (in part)

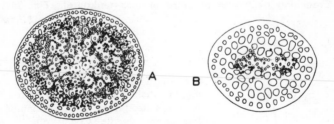

Figure 73

Fig. 73. *Gelidium crinale* (Turner) Lamouroux

Transections of parts of two different plants to show (A.) the aggregation of rhizoidal filaments in the central region of the medulla, and (B.) the aggregation in the outer region of the medulla. The latter is the more common situation encountered in *Gelidium*. This is a rather small, tufted plant reaching 5-7 cm. in height along both the

Atlantic and Pacific coasts. Most of the species of *Gelidium* are flattened (step 185b), but the southern California *G. nudifrons* and some of the larger forms of *G. crinale* are only slightly compressed as indicated in the figures.

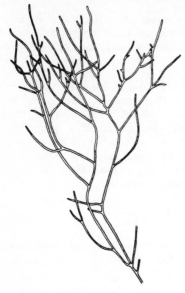

Fig. 74. *Gelidium nudifrons* Gardner

A small portion of a plant about 18 cm. high to show the slender, subcylindrical form and the rather remote branches, × 0.8. Frequent in southern California and sometimes abundant enough in the sublittoral *Gelidium* beds to be used supplementarily for the making of agar.

Figure 74

45b Medulla without rhizoidal filaments..........................46

46a Branching distichous or more or less unilateral. Fig. 75.......
....*Microcladia*

Fig. 75. *Microcladia coulteri* Harvey

A small upper portion of a plant showing the distichous branching of the slightly compressed axes, × 3.2. Common along the entire Pacific Coast, often together with similar *M. californica* Farlow. A third species with unilateral branching, *M. borealis* Ruprecht, occurs from central California northward.

Figure 75

47a Parenchymatous medulla with a central core of relatively slender, longitudinal filaments. Fig. 76.........*Cystoclonium purpureum*

Fig. 76. *Cystoclonium purpureum* (Hudson) Batters

A small upper portion of a female plant showing the multifarious branching and the presence of swellings in some branches representing cystocarps, × 1.2. Grows attached to shells and rocks at low tide level, New Jersey and northward. Mature plants reach 10-50 cm. in height.

Figure 76

48a Older parts of axes with a thin cortex; ultimate branches of variable length, indeterminate. Fig. 77.........*Dictyosiphon* (in part)

Fig. 77. *Dictyosiphon foeniculaceus* (Hudson) Greville

A small portion of a plant about 40 cm. high to show the indeterminate character of the branches, × 1.2. This is a widespread and variable species throughout the entire north Atlantic area, having been described from England nearly 200 years ago. It is a common epiphyte on various algae, especially *Chordaria*, and reaches its best development in summer, although it may be found throughout the year. In our area it is most abundant in New England, but occurs as far south as New Jersey. Some forms tend to be hollow and may key out best under step 95a.

Figure 77

48b Older parts of axes with a thick cortex; ultimate branches usually of similar length, at least more or less determinate. Fig. 78....
....*Rhodomela*

Fig. 78.

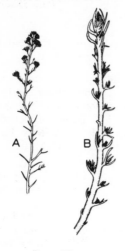

Small portions of two species of *Rhodomela* to show the production of determinate ultimate branchlets from the cylindrical axes. A. *Rhodomela subfusca* (Woodward) C. Agardh, the most widespread of the three New England species. The spring form is illustrated in which the tufted appearance of the tips is prominent. This aspect may in part be lost later in the season by the eroding away of some of these small branchlets. B. *Rhodomela larix* (Turner) C. Agardh, the common Pacific Coast species from central California northward. A young axis is represented in which the ultimate branchlets are much less abundant and congested than in older plants. Both figures $\times$ 1.2.

Figure 78

49a Thalli creeping; indeterminate (compound) branchlets alternating regularly with small series of determinate (simple) branches. Fig. 79 ....*Herposiphonia*

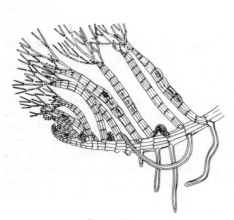

Fig. 79. *Herposiphonia tenella* (C. Agardh) Ambronn

Part of a creeping axis showing attachment rhizoids and the series of three simple, erect, determinate branches alternating with single short, compound indeterminate branches, $\times$ 50. This is the commonest of four species of this genus occurring from North Carolina through Florida. Several other species occur along the Pacific Coast.

Figure 79

They are usually quite small plants but may be conspicuous as epiphytes or in low algal mats or turfs.

Figure 80

Fig. 80. A species of *Polysiphonia* with four pericentral cells (only two of which are usually visible) and showing some short trichoblasts from the scar-cells.

Polysiphonia is a very large genus of relatively small and (or) delicate plants of which about 20 species may be encountered along the Pacific Coast and at least as many along the Atlantic. Some have only four pericentral cells like Figure 80, while others have five to many. The plants may be epiphytic or saxicolous and from as much as 30 cm. tall to as little as a few millimeters. See also Fig. 54A.

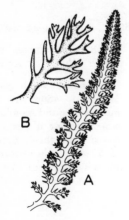

Fig. 81. *Pterosiphonia dendroidea* (Montagne) Falkenberg

A. An erect axis to show the percurrent character and regular, alternate, pinnate branching, × 3.5. B. Detail of a single compound pinna, × 35. This is a common small saxicolous plant along the whole Pacific Coast. Several other species occur from southern California northward, but apparently there are none on the Atlantic Coast.

B

A

Figure 81

51b Percurrent axes not clearly developed. Fig. 82......*Pterochondria*

Fig. 82. *Pterochondria woodii* (Harvey) Hollenberg

A. A small part of a plant about 10 cm. high to show absence of a distinct percurrent axis and the relatively wide spacing of the branches compared to *Pterosiphonia* in Fig. 81, × 3.5. B. Detail of a compound ultimate branchlet, × 16. A common epiphyte on *Cystoseira* and other large algae along the whole Pacific Coast.

Figure 82

52a Thallus with midrib and (or) veins..........................53

52b Thallus without midrib or veins............................55

53a Plants green, with palmate veins. Fig. 83....*Anadyomene stellata*

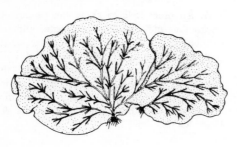

Fig. 83. *Anadyomene stellata* (Wulfen) J. Agardh

An entire small plant, × 0.8, to show the palmate veins and membranous character. Blades may reach a height or spread of 5-7 cm. It is a tropical plant of southern Florida.

Figure 83

53b Plants reddish, with a midrib.................................54
54a Thallus simple, without macroscopic lateral veins. Fig. 84......
....*Grinnellia americana*

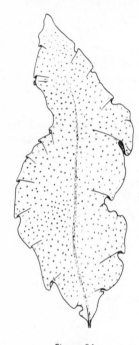

Fig. 84. *Grinnellia americana* (C. Agardh) Harvey

A single blade of an asexual plant to show the simple, ruffled character, absence of lateral veins from the midrib, and the small tetrasporangial sori, × 0.8. This is an attractive plant of pleasing color and form which is sure to appear in summer collections from our north central Atlantic Coast. It inhabits warm quiet water in wading depths at low tide, maturing and disappearing by late summer. It may be encountered from South Carolina to as far north as northern Massachusetts.

Figure 84

54b Thallus pinnately lobed; midrib with distinct, opposite lateral veins. Fig. 85 ....*Phycodrys*

Fig. 85. *Phycodrys rubens* (Hudson) Batters

A single blade to show lobing and veination, × 1. This is the only species of the genus on the Atlantic Coast, occurring from New Jersey northward, especially north of Cape Cod. The common Pacific species is *P. setchellii* found in California and Oregon.

Figure 85

69

56a Thallus mono- to distromatic throughout, purplish; growth intercalary; reproductive structures in marginal areas, not forming
spots. Fig. 86...*Porphyra*

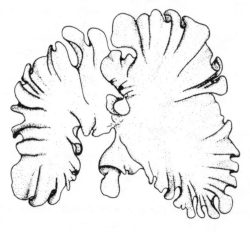

Figure 86

Fig. 86. *Porphyra perforata* J. Agardh

An entire small plant to show the ruffled character resulting from
intercalary growth of the membranous blade, $\times$ 0.75. This monostromatic species is common on middle intertidal rocks along the whole
Pacific Coast. It is an edible species similar to the porphyras cultivated
for food in Japan. It has been extensively harvested in some parts of
California, as much as 300,000 dry pounds being collected in a year.
Several other species of the genus occur as epiphytes or on rocks
along the Pacific and Atlantic coasts but must be identified specifically
by means of the various local floras.

56b Thallus monostromatic at the margins and of more than one cell in thickness in older mid-parts and lower parts, reddish in color; growth marginal; reproductive organs scattered over the blades in small circular or elongate spots. Fig. 87........*Myriogramme*

Fig. 87. *Myriogramme spectabilis* (Eaton) Kylin

A single forked blade of a tetrasporangial plant showing the elongated tetrasporangial sori, × 0.6. This is our largest and commonest species of *Myriogramme*. It normally grows below low tide level along the California coast and is to be looked for in beach drift. There are several other localized species on the Pacific Coast.

Figure 87

57a Thallus 2 cells thick. Fig. 88 A...........................*Ulva*

57b Thallus 1 cell thick. Fig. 88 B.....................*Monostroma*

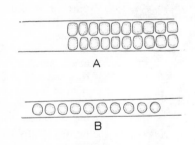

A

B

Figure 88

Fig. 88. Transections of *Ulva* (A.) and of *Monostroma* (B.) to show different appearance of monostromatic and distromatic structure.

A considerable number of species of each of these genera occurs both on the Atlantic and Pacific coasts. The species are widespread and in many cases cosmopolitan. The best means of identifying our Pacific species at present is found in the volume by Setchell and Gardner, 1920, while Taylor, 1937, treats most of the Atlantic species. All of the members of each of these genera are thin, expanded, membranous plants varying in size from a centimeter or two up to more than two meters. In form they resemble the *Porphyra* plant shown in Figure 86.

58a Thallus of varied form and branching, but without cellular septation. Figs. 89, 90...59

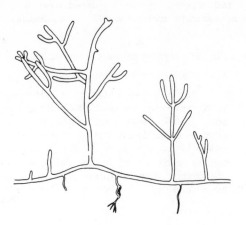

Fig. 89. *Caulerpa
fastigiata* Mon-
tagne

Part of a plant
extracted from a
turf to show the
prostrate and
erect parts and
the descending
rhizoids, all with-
out cellular sep-
tation, × 7.
Sandy places in
Florida.

Figure 89

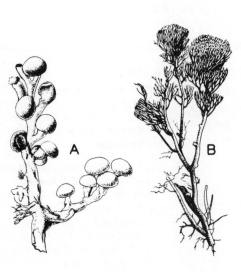

Fig. 90. *Caulerpa*
species to show
varied form
and branching.

A. *Caulerpa
verticillata* J.
Agardh. A small
part of a plant,
× 5. B. *Caulerpa
racemosa* (Forsk-
al) J. Agardh. A
small portion of
a plant, × 1.5.
Both of these spe-
cies and about
eleven others are
to be found in
the warm waters
of the Florida
coasts. Some of
them are flat-
tened and either
subsimple or pin-

Figure 90

nately branched. These will be encountered farther on in the key at
steps 148 and 160.

58b Thallus regularly or irregularly septate..................... 60

59a Thallus traversed internally by a network of trabeculae. Figs. 89, 90, 91.................................*Caulerpa* (in part)

Fig. 91. *Caulerpa* sp.

Transection of an axis to show the internal network of trabeculae, × 9.

Figure 91

59b Thallus not traversed internally by a network of trabeculae. Fig. 92 ....*Bryopsis*

Fig. 92. *Bryopsis pennata* Lamouroux

The terminal portion of a young axis, × 22. At least four species of this genus are to be found along the Atlantic coast, two of them (*B. hypnoides* Lamouroux and *B. plumosa* (Hudson) C. Agardh) extending as far north as New England. Although no species of *Caulerpa* is encountered on our Pacific Coast, several kinds of *Bryopsis* may be found there including the two New England species mentioned above. Both pinnate and multifarious branching occur in the genus.

Figure 92

60a Branching radially symmetrical; branchlets whorled........... 61

60b Branched or unbranched; if branches present, these not whorled.62

61a Gametangia between (enclosed by) cells of secondary whorls. **Fig. 93**....................................*Dasycladus vermicularis*

Fig. 93. *Dasycladus vermicularis* (Scopoli) Krasser

A single lateral branchlet showing the gametangium enclosed by cells of a secondary whorl, $\times$ 17. Growing on shells, coral, etc., in Florida.

Figure 93

61b Gametangia outside of cells of secondary whorls. Fig. 94......
....*Batophora oerstedi*

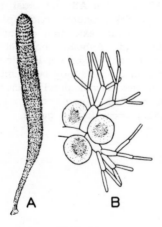

Fig. 94. *Batophora oerstedi* J. Agardh

A. An entire plant of a densely branched form closely resembling *Dasycladus* but showing near the tip an indication of the whorled arrangement of the lateral branchlets, $\times$ 1.1. B. A single lateral branch bearing three gametangia, $\times$ 17. Common in southern Florida and west to Texas.

Figure 94

74

62a Branched filaments consisting of a very few large, vacuolate cells. Fig. 95...*Valonia* (in part)

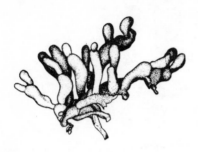

Figure 95

Fig. 95. *Valonia aegagropila* C. Agardh

A small part of a matted plant, × 3. *Valonia* is a tropical genus of several species of variable form from single, very large cells (See Fig. 163) to clusters or coarse filaments of large cells. Five species may be encountered in Florida.

62b Filaments branched or unbranched, of many cells.............63

63a Filaments unbranched, rarely branched, or with few short, simple branchlets 64

63b Filaments normally much-branched.........................68

64a Cells with a single parietal, bracelet-shaped chloroplast. Fig. 96. ....*Ulothrix*

Figure 96

Fig. 96. *Ulothrix implexa* Kützing

A small portion of a filament to show cell shape and form of the chloroplast, × 600 (Note the very small diameter).

Grows as soft, silky tufts on rocks or woodwork along both coasts. There are three other species which may be encountered in our cooler, northern waters.

64b Cells with greatly reticulate or fragmented chloroplasts........65

65a Filaments attached at the base.............................66

65b Filaments free, floating or entangled.........................67

66a Rhizoids, if present, produced only from the basal cell. Fig. 97..
....*Chaetomorpha* (in part)

Fig. 97. *Chaetomorpha antennina* (Bory) Kützing

A. Part of a young plant to show basal attachment and presence of rhizoids arising from the basal cell, × 9. B. A portion of a tuft, × 1.5. This is a southern California representative of this genus which occurs widely on exposed rocks along both coasts. (See also Fig. 100.) It shows the tufted, gregarious habit of the filaments of the basally attached members of this genus of which *C. aerea* (Dillwyn) Kützing is a more widespread but much more slender species. *C. melagonium* (Weber & Mohr) Kützing, from New England, is a similarly coarse species.

Figure 97

76

66b Rhizoids produced from several cells near the base. Fig. 98......
....*Urospora*

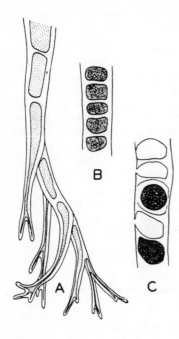

Fig. 98. *Urospora penicilliformis* (Roth) Areschoug

A. The basal part of a plant to show the rhizoids arising from several lower cells, × 220. B., C. Two stages in the production of zoospores in older parts of filaments, × 300. This is perhaps the commonest of several species occurring in New England and along the Pacific Coast from central California northward. They grow on rocks or woodwork as fine, green, silky tufts up to 10 cm. long or more.

Figure 98

67a Filaments 70 μ or less in diameter, unbranched, or with a few short lateral branches. Fig. 99....................*Rhizoclonium*

Figure 99

Fig. 99. *Rhizoclonium kerneri* Stockmayer

A small part of a filament to show the diameter and cell shape, × 235. This is one of several species which may be found widely along any of our coasts.

67b Filaments 100-1000 μ in diameter, unbranched. Fig. 100.......
...*Chaetomorpha* (in part)

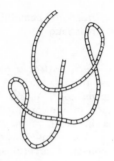

Fig. 100. *Chaetomorpha linum* (Müller) Kützing

A small part of an entangled filament, × 4. One of three free, drifting or entangled species occurring along the Atlantic Coast. Others may be found on Pacific shores of which one of the most striking is the southern Californian *C. torta* (Farlow) McClatchie which is very coarse (over 1 mm.) and strongly coiled or twisted.

Figure 100

68a Color greenish, usually grass green.........................69

68b Color reddish or brownish, not grass green or greenish........71

69a Lower parts of plants held together by rhizoidal, hooked or spine-like branchlets. Fig. 101........................*Spongomorpha*

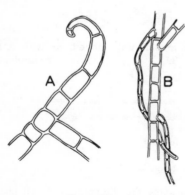

Fig. 101. *Spongomorpha* spp.

A. *Spongomorpha coalita* (Ruprecht) Collins. The end of a branch showing a hook, × 30. Central California and northward. B. *Spongomorpha arcta* (Dillwyn) Kützing. A lower part of an axis showing the production of descending, entwining rhizoids, × 30. This plant forms hemispherical tufts on exposed rocks along the New England coast. Several other species occur along the northern shores of both coasts.

Figure 101

69b Filaments free, not held together by special branchlets, although
    sometimes somewhat twisted.................................70

70a Cell walls present at the base of each branch. Fig. 102..........
    ....*Cladophora*

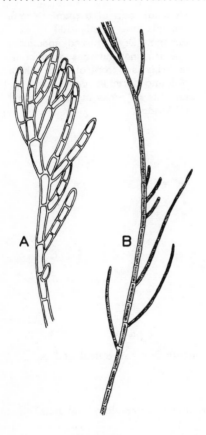

Figure 102

Fig. 102. *Cladophora* spp.

    A. *Cladophora trichoto-ma* (C. Agardh) Kützing. A small upper, branched portion of a plant, × 25. A common, coarse, tufted species along the Pacific Coast. A dozen or more other species may be encountered along the Pacific and may be identified through the use of keys in Setchell & Gardner, 1920. B. *Cladophora albida* (Hudson) Kützing. A small portion of a branched axis, × 50. This is an example of one of the several very delicate forms which may be found either along the Atlantic or Pacific coasts. This one, although so delicate, may reach 10 cm. in height.

70b Base of upper branches usually without a cross wall. Fig. 103...
.................................*Cladophoropsis membranacea*

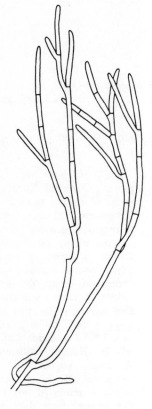

Fig. 103. *Cladophoropsis membranacea* (C. Agardh) Börgesen

A small part of a plant, $\times$ 9.6. The filaments are mostly 100 to 200 μ in diameter. Dry, pressed specimens will appear rather lustrous against the paper. This is a tropical plant which may be found forming dense, soft patches and tufts on rocks in rather quiet water in Florida.

Figure 103

71a Thallus reddish in color; growth from an apical cell..........**74**

71b Thallus brownish in color; growth intercalary, not from an apical cell **72**

72a Erect filaments all more or less alike; plants epiphytic or saxicalous **73**

72b Erect filaments of two kinds: crowded, short, moniliform filaments below, and long, straight, free filaments extending above; plants epiphytic. Fig. 104..................................*Elachista*

Fig. 104. *Elachista fucicola* (Velley) Areschoug

A very small bit of a sterile tuft showing the two kinds of filaments, × 80. This is a common epiphyte on coarse algae from New Jersey northward and from central Oregon northward. Two other species occur on the New England coast on *Chondrus, Ascophyllum,* and other coarse algae. The tufts are small, usually under 2 cm. high, but are often abundant and conspicuous.

Figure 104

73a Reproductive organs in a series in the middle of a filament. Fig. 105 ....*Pylaiella*

Figure 105

Fig. 105. *Pylaiella litoralis* (Linnaeus) Kjellman

A small portion of a fertile filament showing the serial and inter-calary production of unilocular sporangia, × 180. Commonly 5-25 cm. long on various substrates from New Jersey northward and from central California northward along the Pacific. Other species may occur, but are rare or of local distribution.

81

73b Reproductive organs lateral or terminal on the filaments. Fig. 106.
....*Ectocarpus*

Fig. 106. *Ectocarpus* spp.

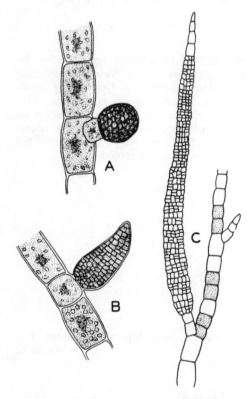

Figure 106

Three different examples of types of plurilocular sporangia characteristic of *Ectocarpus* are shown (A-B, × 200; C, × 225). In C the stippled cells indicate those in which intercalary division has most recently occurred. *Ectocarpus* is a large genus of relatively small plants. One or more species may be found almost anywhere, often as epiphytes, but except for a few kinds they do not reach conspicuous size. The local floras must be used for the identification of species.

74a Branching opposite, at least in major part. Fig. 107.. *Antithamnion*

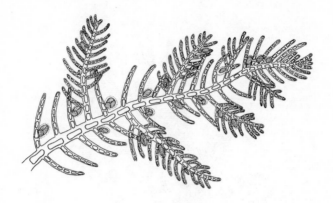

Figure 107

Fig. 107. *Antithamnion* sp.

A small upper part of a fertile plant showing the opposite branching and the position of tetrasporangia, $\times$ 80. This is a large genus of very delicate, beautiful plants which are commonly epiphytic. Some species are quite small, while others reach 20 cm. in height. They may be encountered on any part of our coasts and must be identified specifically through the use of the various local floras.

74b Branching alternate, dichotomous or irregular (sometimes partly or wholly opposite in *Spermothamnion turneri*)................75

75a Branching regularly alternate, normally with a branch from each
cell of the main axis, at least above. Fig. 108..................76

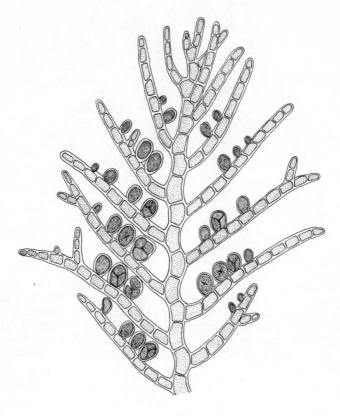

Figure 108

Fig. 108. *Callithamnion rupicolum* Anderson

A small upper portion of a fertile plant showing regular alternate
branching from each cell of the main axis and the production of tetrasporangia, × 120. A common small species along the California coast.

This is a moderately large genus of delicate plants of which one
or more species may be found along most any part of our coasts.
Some of the coarser and more or less corticated species will key out
under step 31b.

75b Branching not regularly alternate, or at least without a branch from each cell of the main axis. Fig. 109 77

Fig. 109. *Spermothamnion turneri* (Mertens) Areschoug

A small upper portion of a fertile plant showing multifarious branching and presence of axial cells without branches, × 75. This is a common small epiphyte on *Chondrus* and *Phyllophora* in infratidal waters along the Atlantic Coast south of Cape Cod. It may be 2 to 5 cm. tall and is usually found in summer in tetrasporic condition. Note that another species of *Spermothamnion* from the Pacific Coast (See Fig. 112) has distinctive polysporangia.

Figure 109

76a Asexual plants bearing tetrasporangia. (See Fig. 108) ....
....*Callithamnion*
(In part; see also step 31b and Figure 52)

76b Asexual plants bearing polysporangia. Fig. 110.... *Pleonosporium*

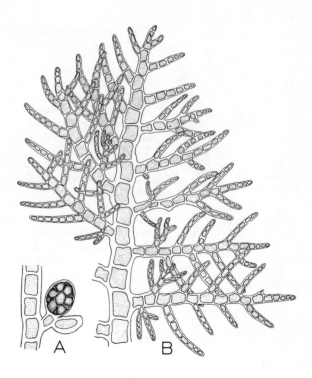

Figure 110

Fig. 110. *Pleonosporium dasyoides* (J. Agardh) De Toni

A. A small upper part of a sterile plant showing the regular, alternate branching, × 56. B. A polysporangium,, × 72. This is our largest member of the genus, reaching 20 cm. in height along the central California coast. The somewhat smaller *P. borreri* (J. E. Smith) Nägeli occurs from Florida to Cape Cod. Several other relatively local species may be found along the Pacific Coast.

77a Branching more or less clearly dichotomous or trichotomous, the
cells large enough to be visible to the naked eye. Fig. 111......
....*Griffithsia*

Fig. 111. *Griffithsia pacifica* Kylin

A small upper part of a male
plant, $\times$ 6.4, showing the large
cells and dichotomous branching.
This is the commonest and most
widespread species along the Pacific Coast from Puget Sound to
southern California. *G. globulifera*
Harvey is common along the Atlantic south of Cape Cod and has
cells up to 1.5 mm. in diameter.
G. tenuis C. Agardh, with the same
range, is 5-20 cm. tall but with
slender, elongate cells about 300
μ in diameter or less.

Figure 111

77b Branching irregular, unilateral, alternate, or sometimes opposite;
cells microscopic. Figs. 109, 112................*Spermothamnion*

Fig. 112. *Spermothamnion snyderae* Farlow

A small portion of a plant bearing polysporangia, $\times$ 80. This is the only species of
the genus occurring along the Pacific Coast.
It is a small plant to 5 cm. high growing in
dense tufted masses on rocks from central to
southern California. Unlike the Atlantic *S. turneri*, it has polysporangia. *S. turneri*, our only
Atlantic species, is of similar stature, but is
epiphytic.

Figure 112

78a Thallas perforated, net-like. Fig. 113.....*Hydroclathrus clathratus*

Fig. 113. *Hydroclathrus clathratus* (Bory) Howe

A small portion of a reticulate plant, × 1.5. This is a species of wide tropical distribution which may be encountered in our area along the Florida coast and occasionally in southernmost California.

Figure 113

78b Thallus crustose, not perforated, not net-like.................79

79a Thallus reddish to purplish when wet........................80

79b Thallus dark brownish in color when wet, at least not reddish or purplish 81

80a Thallus firmly adherent, composed of very small, cuboidal cells; tetrasporangia irregularly zonate, borne in cavities. Fig. 114....
..............................*Hildenbrandia prototypus* Nardo

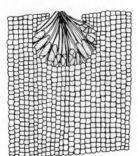

Fig. 114. *Hildenbrandia prototypus* Nardo

A vertical section through a tetrasporangial conceptacle showing the arrangement of the sporangia and the small, cuboidal vegetative cells, × 150. Common along both coasts as a red film on intertidal rocks and on shells.

Note the absence of rhizoids from the basal cell layer in comparing with *Peyssonelia* below.

Figure 114

80b Thallus attached by rhizoids on the under side; cells not especially small; tetrasporangia cruclate, borne in a superficial layer. Fig. 115 ....*Peyssonelia*

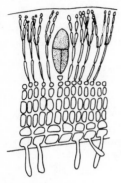

Figure 115

Fig. 115. *Peyssonelia* sp.

A vertical section through a tetrasporangial thallus showing the rhizoids from the basal cell layer and the position of a tetrasporangium in a special, nemathecial, superficial layer (nemathecium). Species of this genus may be encountered encrusting rocks at low intertidal levels, or infratidally, on either of our coasts.

81a Crusts relatively thin, firm, somewhat brittle or woody. Fig. 116. ....*Ralfsia*

Figure 116

Fig. 116. *Ralfsia* sp.

An example of a loosely attached form showing concentric lines of growth, $\times$ 1. A number of species occur on rocks, some of them very firmly attached and so flat, thin, and dark that they may be mistaken by the layman for patches of tar. Sometimes they completely cover rock surfaces to give the intertidal area a dark brown color. They are widespread along the whole Pacific Coast and in the cooler northern waters along the Atlantic. They are usually at rather high intertidal levels and are resistant to considerable desiccation.

81b Crusts thick, convoluted, spongy. Fig. 117.. *Petrospongium rugosum*

Figure 117

Fig. 117. *Petrospongium rugosum* (Oka-mura) Setchell & Gardner

An entire plant showing the convoluted appearance, × 1. Common on upper intertidal rocks of central and southern California.

82a Thallus not erect, but sub-spherical, hemispherical, or expanded and convoluted; surface smooth or warty.....................83

82b Thallus not as above, erect..................................85

83a Thallus green, composed of macroscopic cells. Fig. 118.........
.... *Dictyosphaeria cavernosa*

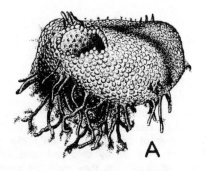

A   B

Figure 118

Fig. 118. *Dictyosphaeria cavernosa* (Forskål) Börgesen

A. Habit of an entire small plant with a portion cut out to show the hollow character, × 3.2. B. Detail of several of the macroscopic cells, × 12.8.

Frequent on exposed rocks along the Florida coast.

84a Thallus slippery, structurally composed of branched filaments. Fig. 119 ....*Leathesia*

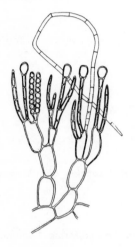

Fig. 119. *Leathesia difformis* (Linnaeus) Areschoug

A small portion of the outer tissues of a plant to show the filamentous structure which includes vegetative filaments, paraphyses, gametangia and a hair, × 240. This is a common, small, subspherical plant on rocks and algae, especially on *Corallina*. It occurs along the entire Pacific Coast and in the cooler Atlantic waters north of North Carolina. Only one other local California species of the genus grows within our area.

Figure 119

84b Thallus not slippery, crisp, structurally composed of parenchymatous cells. Fig. 120 ....*Colpomenia sinuosa*

Fig. 120. *Colpomenia sinuosa* (Roth) Derbès & Solier

Habit of a subspherical plant, × 1.5. This plant may be encountered in Florida and in the summer along most any part of the Pacific Coast especially in waters subject to marked warming. It is exceedingly variable, from small, spherical epiphytic plants to large, broad, prostrate or floating ones in which the hollow form has reached a state of collapse.

Figure 120

85a Thallus a simple sac to 3 cm. in diameter. Figs. 121, 122......86

85b Thallus not a simple sac...................................87

86a Plant saxicolous. Fig. 121..............*Halosaccion glandiforme*

Fig. 121. *Halosaccion glandiforme* (Gmelin) Ruprecht.

An entire medium size plant, $\times$ 0.75. Common on rocks along the Pacific Coast except in southern California. The large finger-shaped sack is filled with water when the plants are young and intact. When compressed, however, the water spurts out from microscopic openings near the tip in a number of very fine jets. Old plants become eroded and the sack more or less filled with sand. This curious alga, described from Kamschatka in 1768, was one of the first seaweeds recorded in the scientific literature from the North Pacific.

Figure 121

86b Plants epiphytic; sacs sometimes so flattened as to appear blade-like. Fig. 122 . . . .*Coilodesme*

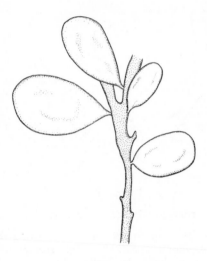

Figure 122

Fig. 122. *Coilodesme rigida* Setchell & Gardner

Several plants growing on a piece of *Halidrys*, × 0.8 Five species occur more or less locally along the Pacific Coast. This one is occasional in southern California while the commonest and most widespread one, *C. californica* (Ruprecht) Kjellman occurs on *Cystoseira* from central California northward.

87a Thallus hollow-tubular, at least in older parts, and of uniform structure throughout. Fig. 124 88

87b Thallus not of uniform structure throughout, with differentiation of parts 96

88a Thallus regularly constricted and with diaphragms at the constrictions. Fig. 123.....................................*Champia*

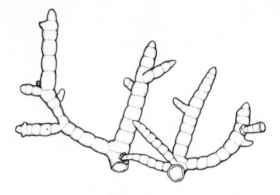

Figure 123

Fig. 123. *Champia parvula* (C Agardh) Harvey

A portion of a plant of caespitose form showing the constrictions of the thallus at the diaphragms, $\times$ 7. This species is frequent along the Atlantic coast from Florida to Cape Cod, usually in dense tufts 3-7 cm. tall. The more strongly constricted C. *salicornioides* Harvey may be found in Florida.

88b Thallus smooth, or if constricted, without diaphragms.........89

89a Wall of tubular thallus only 1 cell thick (Fig. 124); color greenish. Fig. 125 ....*Enteromorpha*

Fig. 124. *Enteromorpha* sp.

A transection of an axis to show the single layer of cells and the hollow structure.

Figure 124

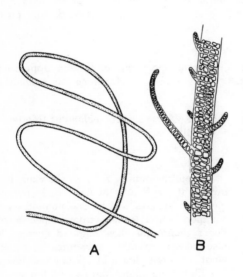

A

Figure 125

B

Fig. 125. *Enteromorpha* spp.

A. *Enteromorpha tubulosa* (Kützing) Kützing. A portion of an unbranched, hairlike filament, × 7. B. *Enteromorpha clathrata* (Roth) Greville. A small part of an axis with several uniseriate branchlets, × 80. This genus contains some of the most widespread and cosmopolitan of the marine algae. Many species may be found on either coast, and in a great diversity of habitats. Most of them are exceedingly variable in form and some are notoriously difficult to identify. *E. linza* (Linnaeus) J. Agardh is a species which is flattened in upper parts like *Ulva*, but hollow at the base like *Enteromorpha*.

89b Wall of tubular thallus more than 1 cell thick; color brownish or reddish **90**

90a Thallus little or not at all branched except at the base........91

90b Thallus branched throughout...............................94

91a Plants less than ½ meter long; hairs, if present, in tufts........92

91b Plants usually more than ½ meter long (1-5 meters); thallus surface covered with fine hairs, at least on young parts. (See Fig.
32)..*Chorda* (in part)

92a Thallus unconstricted; groups of sporangia and hairs appearing
as dark flecks. Fig. 126.................*Asperococcus echinatus*

Fig. 126. *Asperococcus echinatus* (Mertens)
Greville

An entire plant, × 1.5, showing the
abundant small tufts of hairs and sporangia. This species will be encountered as a
common epiphyte on various species of
Fucus along the New England coasts. It
also occurs on other substrates in somewhat sheltered places below low tide level.
It will not be found throughout the year,
for the plants mature and fruit during the
spring and by midsummer have largely decayed and disappeared.

Figure 126

92b Thallus constricted or unconstricted, without groups of sporangia
and hairs aggregated in tufts and appearing as dark flecks....93

96

93a Thallus commonly constricted, brown in color, totally unbranched.
Fig. 127 . . . . *Scytosiphon lomentaria*

Fig. 127. *Scytosiphon lomentaria* (Lyngbye) C.
Agardh

An entire plant of one of the larger, clearly
constricted forms, $\times$ 0.5. This is a common
plant along both the Pacific and Atlantic coasts,
and occurs in a variety of forms in different
habitats. Some forms, especially at high intertidal levels may be unconstricted. Among these
there are both slender cylindrical forms and
some which are quite strongly flattened, although hollow. The brown color and unbranched
habit are distinctive.

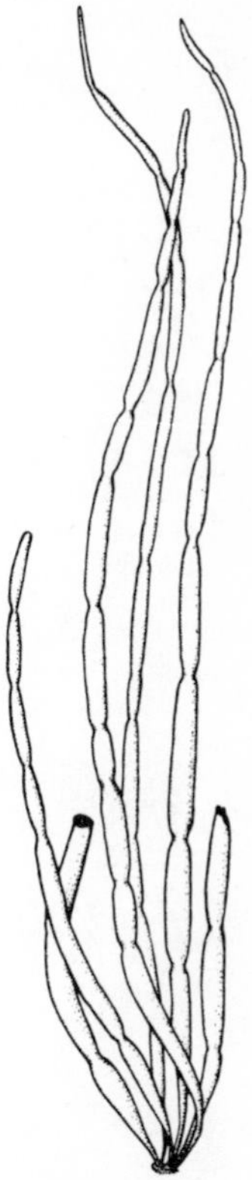

93b Thallus not constricted although often of
somewhat irregular diameter, reddish or
purplish in color, occasionally branched at
the base and sometimes proliferous above.
Fig. 128 . . . . *Halosaccion ramentaceum*

Figure 127

Fig. 128. *Halosaccion ramentaceum* (Linnaeus) J.
Agardh

Part of a plant showing branching of lower
stipe part and the beginning of some proliferations from one tubular axis, $\times$ 0.8. Plants of this
species are gregarious on stones and shells near
low water mark from northern Massachusetts
through Maine. They may reach 30-40 cm. long.

Figure 128

97

94a Axes and (or) branches 2-5 mm. in diameter; cortex, as seen in transection, composed of anticlinally arranged, branched filaments of short cells. Fig. 129......................*Dumontia incrassata*

Figure 129

Fig. 129. *Dumontia incrassata* (Müller) Lamouroux

An entire, medium size plant, $\times$ 1, showing the hollow branches of rather large diameter. Grows in tide pools or just below low tide level along the New England coast from Rhode Island northward. The species is especially interesting in that it apparently was introduced to the New England coast and became established only a few decades ago. The first collection was made at South Harpswell, Maine in June, 1913. Since then it has been found more and more commonly at a number of localities from Rhode Island to Nova Scotia.

94b Axes and branches usually 1 mm. or less in diameter; cortex as seen in transection composed of more or less isodiametrical cells without evident arrangement in rows or filaments............95

95a Thallus brownish; percurrent axes evident; medulla only partially hollow, or only in older parts. (See Fig. 77)..*Dictyosiphon* (in part)

95b Thallus reddish; percurrent axes usually not evident; medulla hollow throughout, although sometimes with filaments around the cavity. Fig. 130...........................*Lomentaria baileyana*

Figure 130

Fig. 130. *Lomentaria baileyana* (Harvey) Farlow

Part of a plant to show the slender form and lack of percurrent axes, $\times$ 1.2. This species is usually loosely tufted, 3 to 7 cm. high, in sheltered places from Cape Cod to Florida.

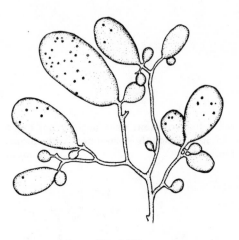

Figure 131

Fig. 131. *Botryocladia pseudodichotoma* (Farlow) Kylin

Part of a fertile, cystocarpic plant, × 1. Although usually of sub-littoral occurrence, this plant may frequently be found in beach drift along the entire Pacific Coast. It is conspicuous because of its peculiar form and bright red color, and has received the common name of "Sea Grapes." In making pressed specimens the collector will do well to puncture the hollow, turgid vesicles in order to allow them to flatten in the press as their liquid contents are extruded. Otherwise they may burst in the process to give an unnatural appearance to the dry specimen.

97b Solid axes bearing hollow, cylindrical, constricted branchlets with diaphragms at the constrictions. Fig. 132...*Gastroclonium coulteri*

Figure 132

Fig. 132. *Gastroclonium coulteri* (Harvey) Kylin

A small upper portion of a plant to show the solid axis and the hollow, constricted, lateral branchlets, $\times$ 1.6. Frequent on rocks along virtually the entire Pacific Coast. The degree of development of the hollow lateral branchlets varies so that one should expect occasionally to find specimens in which these are scanty, much reduced, or otherwise inconspicuous. Close inspection, however, will invariably reveal the transverse septa at the constrictions in some of these hollow branchlets.

98a Thallus with a single large, hollow bulb (pneumatocyst) at the end of a long, unbranched stipe (See Fig. 134)..............99

98b Plants with more than one hollow structure.................100

99a **Apex of pneumatocyst with four short, flattened branches which are four to five times dichotomous. Fig. 133..***Nereocystis luetkeana*

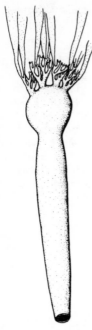

Fig. 133. *Nereocystis luetkeana* (Mertens) Postels & Ruprecht

A pneumatocyst showing the bulbous, ter, minal swelling and four dichotomous, blade-bearing branches, × 0.2. This is a giant kelp which grows in great beds from rocks 30 to 50 feet below the surface, sending up the pneumatocysts and blades which float out at the surface. Common along the Pacific Coast except in southernmost California.

Figure 133

99b **Apex of pneumatocyst with a single large antler-like, forked branch. Fig. 134............................***Pelagophycus porra*

Fig. 134. *Pelagophycus porra* (Leman) Setchell

Habit of an entire plant, × 0.04, showing the holdfast, long, rising stipe and blade-bearing terminal pneumatocyst. This is probably our most spectacular large Pacific coast kelp. It occupies habitats outside the *Macrocystis* beds in somewhat deeper water and is avoided by the commercial kelp cutters. Its range extends from Point Conception, California southward into Mexico.

Figure 134

100a Vesicles produced by inflation of portions of flat, dichotomous blades. Fig. 135............................*Fucus vesiculosus*

Fig. 135. *Fucus vesiculosus* Linnaeus

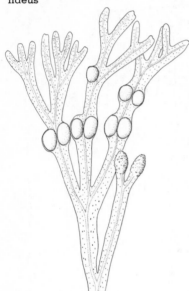

An upper part of a plant to show the dichotomous branching and the vesicles which are usually paired, × 0.56. This is one of the commonest of all the marine algae along the Atlantic Coast from North Carolina northward. *Fucus evanescens* C. Agardh is a north Pacific coast species having vesicles, but other members of this common genus lack vesicles and are treated elsewhere in this key (See step 135).

Figure 135

100b Vesicles not produced in flat, dichotomous blades............101

101a Vesicles borne on either side of flat, ligulate, percurrent axes. Fig. 136..*Egregia*

Fig. 136. *Egregia laevigata* Setchell

A. Habit of an entire plant, × 0.04. B. A small portion of one of the flat axes bearing lateral blades many of which have vesicles at their bases, × 0.5. This is one of the large brown algae of central and southern California which attracts the most attention because of its peculiar form and its abundance along some bathing beaches. It has been called the "Feather Boa." Another species, *E. menziesii* (Turner) Areschoug, is similar in habit but occurs from central California northward to Canada.

Figure 136

101b Vesicles not distichous..................................102

102a Vesicles borne in series..................................103

102b Vesicles solitary..104

103a Seriate vesicles compressed. Fig. 137............*Halidrys dioica*

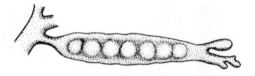

Figure 137

Fig. 137. *Halidrys dioica* Gardner

A single series of vesicles showing the flattened character, × 1.8. Note that some forms may have a less pronounced blade-like development than is shown in the figure.

Halidrys is vegetatively similar to *Cystoseira* (See Fig. 138) and may be confused with members of that genus in the absence of the readily recognizable vesicles. The only species, *H. dioica,* is restricted to southern California, while species of *Cystoseira* extend farther north.

103b Seriate vesicles spherical and catenate. Fig. 138......*Cystoseira*

Fig. 138. *Cystoseira osmundacea* (Menzies) C. Agardh

Habit of a short, intertidal form of this species to show the holdfast, leaf-like blades, and catenate vesicles, × 0.5. This is the most widespread of three species of this genus on our Pacific Coast, extending throughout California to central Oregon. Many plants, especially infratidal ones, are much more lax in habit than the plant illustrated. Central California plants are reported to reach a length of 7.5 meters. Entangled pieces of *Cystoseira* are often found in drift along California beaches.

Figure 138

104a Main axes here and there much inflated to form the float bladders. Fig. 139 . . . .*Ascophyllum nodosum*

Fig. 139. *Ascophyllum nodosum* (Linnaeus) Le Jolis

An upper portion of a fertile plant showing hollow vesicles in the main axes and the stalked, club-shaped, deciduous, receptacular branchlets, $\times$ 0.6. A common plant on rocks along the Atlantic Coast to the north of New Jersey.

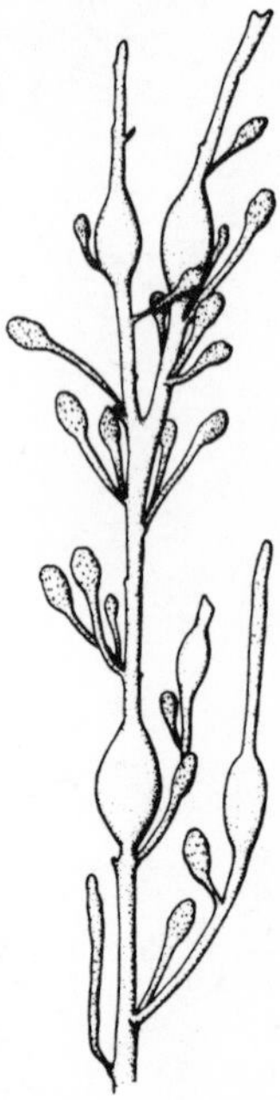

104b Not as above; vesicles free, individually stipitate 105

105a Vesicles large, each bearing an expanded blade. Fig. 140 . . . .*Macrocystis*

Fig. 140. *Macrocystis pyrifera* (Linnaeus) C. Agardh

A. Habit of a sporophyte plant growing in position, $\times$ 0.02. B. A blade with its basal pneumatocyst, $\times$ 0.5. This species grows along our entire Pacific Coast, forming great "kelp beds" which in southern California are so richly developed that commercial exploitation is carried out on a large scale for the production of the valuable phycocolloid *algin* and its derivatives. Harvesting is accomplished by cutting the floating parts of the kelp a few feet below the surface with a large mowing machine installed on a barge upon which the cut kelp is piled for transport to the factory.

Figure 139

Algin is an amazingly versatile, hydrophilic colloid which has recently found numerous uses in industry. Large quantities are used in stabilizing ice cream, chocolate milk, syrups, icings, puddings, sauces, salad dressings, etc. As emulsifying, stabilizing and suspending agents algin products serve in the manufacture of a great variety of products such as tooth paste, lotions, pharmaceutical jelly, film emulsions, textile sizings, paints, boiler compounds, brazing pastes, polishes, insecticides, oil well drilling muds, battery plate separators, etc.

One other species, *M. integrifolia* Bory, distinguished by a flattening of the holdfast parts, is present from central California northward.

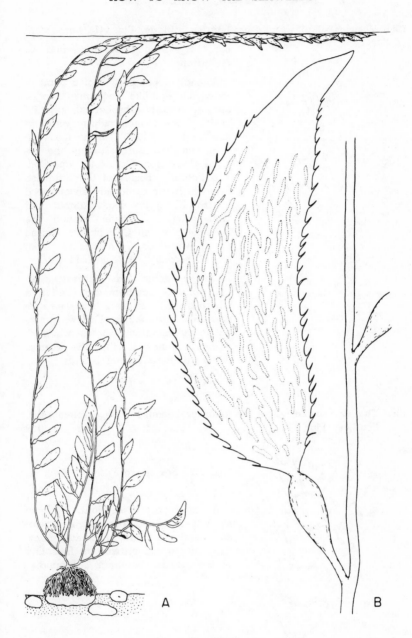

Figure 140

105b Vesicles small, usually not bearing a blade. Fig. 141 Sargassum

Figure 141

Fig. 141. *Sargassum filipendula* C. Agardh

A small upper portion of a plant to show the leaf-like vegetative blades and the small, subspherical, stipitate vesicles, one of them bearing an abortive blade, $\times$ 0.64. This is the common, attached *Sargassum* of the Atlantic Coast from Florida to Cape Cod. The floating species of the Sargasso Sea which are commonly encountered in drift along the south Atlantic and Gulf coasts originate through the movement of the Gulf stream. These are of two kinds, *S. fluitans* Börgesen, and *S. natans* (Linnaeus) J. Meyen.

On the Pacific Coast *Sargassum* occurs only in southernmost California where a small, densely branched species, *S. agardhianum* Farlow, grows on rocky mainland shores while *S. palmeri* Grunow inhabits the warmer waters of the Channel Islands.

106a Thallus flexible, either by joints or because of incomplete calcification.   Fig. 142...109

Fig. 142. *Bossea* sp.

A small part of a plant, $\times$ 5, to show the calcified segments (intergenicula) and the short, uncalcified joints (genicula) which provide for flexibility of the thallus. Southern California.

Figure 142

106b Thallus inflexible, hard and stony throughout. Fig. 143......107

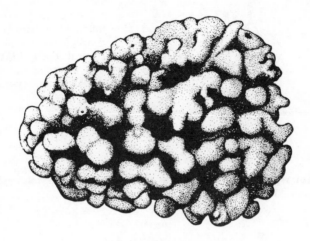

Figure 143

Fig. 143. *Lithothamnium giganteum* L. R. Mason

An entire plant, $\times$ 1.2. This species from southern California is an example of a crustose coralline in which prominent excrescences are produced and in which growth may proceed as the plant, having originated on a loose pebble or piece of shell, is tossed about in the surf or rolls along the sea floor. Numerous other species grow firmly attached to rocks and may have such surface outgrowths or may be only warty or entirely smooth. This range of characters is common also to the genera *Lithophyllum* and *Goniolithon* in which generic distinctions are based upon internal anatomy and reproduction. Although species of *Lithophyllum* and *Lithothamnium* may be found along either the Atlantic or Pacific coasts, *Goniolithon* is as yet recorded from the United States only in the warm waters of Florida.

111

107a Tetrasporangial conceptacles with many small pores formed by
the transformation of rows of cells into gelatinous plugs in the roof
of the conceptacles. Figs. 143, 144...............*Lithothamnium*

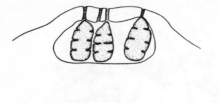

Figure 144

Fig. 144. *Lithothamnium* sp.

Diagrammatic represen-
tation of a tetrasporangial
conceptacle to show the
several pores in the roof
and the form and position
of the zonate tetrasporangia, × 40.

107b Tetrasporangial conceptacles opening by a single, relatively large
pore. Fig. 145...108

108a Tetrasporangia borne over whole floor of conceptacle...........
....*Goniolithon*

108b Tetrasporangia marginal within the conceptacles, the central area
of the floor occupied by paraphyses. Fig. 145......*Lithophyllum*

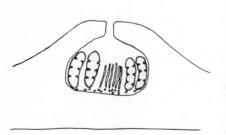

Figure 145

Fig. 145. *Lithophyllum* sp.

Diagrammatic represen-
tation of a tetrasporangial
conceptacle to show the
single large pore in the
roof and the marginal position of the zonate tetrasporangia with a group of
paraphyses occupying the
central area of the con-
ceptacle floor, × 40.

110a Each growing apex bearing a tuft of branched filaments. Fig. 146.
....*Cymopolia barbata*

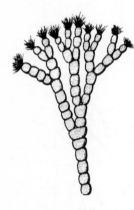

Fig. 146. *Cymopolia barbata* (Linnaeus) Lamouroux

A small upper portion of a plant to show the segmented character and terminal tufts of hairs, × 2. A common plant of shallow water in southern Florida.

Figure 146

110b Apices without tufts of filaments............................111

111a Base of plant with a fibrous holdfast which penetrates sand or mud. Fig. 147....................................*Halimeda*

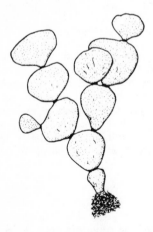

Fig. 147. *Halimeda discoidea* Decaisne

A small plant showing the calcified segments separated by fibrous, flexible joints, and the fibrous holdfast, × 0.75. This is one of several species, all of cactus-like form, which may be encountered in southern Florida.

Figure 147

111b Base of plant solid, calcified, without penetrating filaments. (See remark under Fig. 148)...................................112

112a Segments more than twice as broad as thick. Fig. 148........113

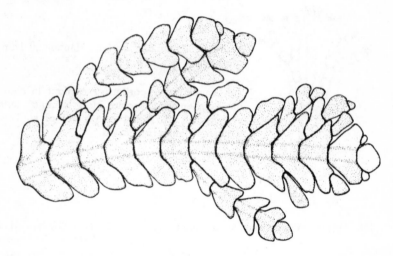

Figure 148

Fig. 148. *Bossea* sp.

A small upper part of a plant to show the broad, winged inter-genicula more than twice as broad as thick. Close inspection of a plant of *Bossea*, or of one of the other articulated coralline genera treated below through step 116, will show that as it grows intact on its rock, or in the case of *Jania*, its host plant, it consists of two parts. The erect, jointed parts are conspicuous, but there is also a thin, crustose film spreading over the rock and adhering completely to it. This basal crust cannot usually be removed with the specimen unless a piece of the rock is taken.

112b Segments cylindrical to compressed, mostly less than twice as broad as thick...114

113a Conceptacles both on margins and on flattened faces of segments. Fig. 149...*Calliarthron*

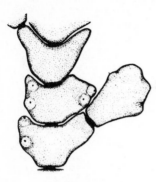

Fig. 149. *Calliarthron cheilosporioides* Manza

A few segments of a plant to show the location of conceptacles both on the margins and on the flattened faces of the segments near the margins, × 4.3. This is one of several species which occur at low tide level or below along the California coast.

Figure 149

113b Conceptacles restricted to flattened faces of segments. Fig. 142, 148, 150...*Bossea*

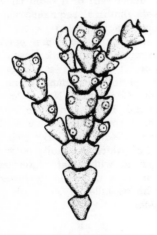

Fig. 150. *Bossea* sp.

A small upper part of a plant showing the position of the conceptacles exclusively on the flattened faces of the intergenicula, × 3.6. Although no species of *Bossea* are known from the Atlantic coast, a number of them may be found along the Pacific, sometimes several in a single locality. They are usually at low levels on surfy shores, and attached to solid substrates.

Figure 150

115

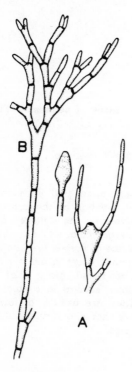

Figure 151

Fig. 151. *Jania tenella* Kützing

A. Two kinds of terminal conceptacles: antheridial on the left, tetrasporangial on the right, × 18. B. A small upper part of a plant showing the subcylindrical segments and the dichotomous branching, × 18. This is a delicate but common epiphyte of our warmer waters along southern California. This and a number of other species are found along the Atlantic Coast from North Carolina southward, but *J. capillacea* Harvey will most commonly be found. It is a very delicate, regularly dichotomous plant which is usually entangled and mixed with other algae rather than in pure growths. Its branches may be as little as 50 to 100 μ in diameter.

115b Branching pinnate. Fig. 152.........................*Corallina*

Fig. 152. *Corallina officinalis* Linnaeus

Part of an example of the large robust Pacific coast form (var. *chilensis*), × 1. Various environmental forms of this species may be encountered along the whole Pacific Coast and from Long Island northward through New England. At least three other species may be found along the Pacific of which the smaller and more densely branched *C. vancouveriensis* Yendo is the most abundant and widespread.

Figure 152

116a Segments very short; intergenicular medulla unizonal. Fig. 153.
....*Lithothrix* aspergillum

Fig. 153. *Lithothrix aspergillum* J. E. Gray

A small portion of a plant bearing a single lateral conceptacle and showing the very short, cylindrical segments (intergenicula) × 5. The unizonal intergenicular medulla can be observed by decalcifying a small piece and crushing it out carefully on a slide so as to make the elongate medullary cells visible.

A common tufted plant 3 to 12 cm. high on rocks and in tide pools along the entire Pacific Coast.

Figure 153

117

116b Segments not particularly short; intergenicular medulla multizonal.
Fig. 154..*Amphiroa*

Figure 154

Fig. 154. *Amphiroa fragilissima* (Linnaeus) Lamouroux

A portion of a loosely branched plant showing the elongated intergenicula separated by conspicuous genicula, × 3. This is the most widespread of our species, occurring from North Carolina to Florida. At least two other species, one of them quite strongly flattened, may be found in Florida. *A. zonata* Yendo is frequent in southern California.

117a Thallus fan-shaped 118

117b Thallus not fan-shaped....................................119

118a Thallus composed of filaments (Fig. 155), moderately calcified. Fig. 156...*Udotea*

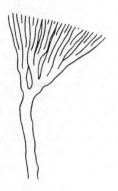

Fig. 155. *Udotea* sp.

The lower part of a small, delicate, exotic species in which the filamentous structure is evident, × 21.

Figure 155

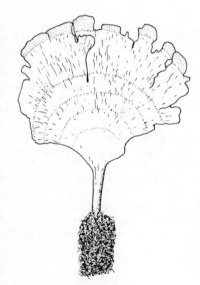

Figure 156. *Udotea flabellum* (Solander) Howe

An entire plant, × 0.7, showing the fan-like form, the concentric lines of growth and the sand-penetrating holdfast. This species may be found in quiet waters from North Carolina southward. Other species are confined to Florida within our territory.

Figure 156

119

118b Thallus composed of parenchymatous cells, lightly calcified superficially, or sometimes apparently uncalcified. Fig. 157..*Padina*

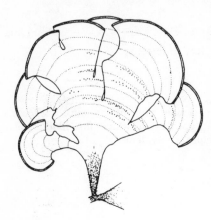

Figure 157

Fig. 157. *Padina vickersiae* Hoyt

A portion of a plant showing the irregularly split blade, the unrolled margins, the concentric hair lines and some rows of sporangia, × 0.65. This is a very lightly calcified species found from North Carolina to Florida and Texas. *P. sanctae-crucis* Börgesen, which is strongly calcified on the under side occurs in southern Florida.

119a Thallus consisting of a simple stalk bearing a disc at the top. Fig. 158 . . . .*Acetabularia*

Figure 158

Fig. 158. *Acetabularia crenulata* Lamouroux

Upper part of a plant, × 3. This is a common and highly attractive green alga on broken coral in quiet water in southern Florida and west to Texas. Even a rusty old coffee can may be found wonderfully glamorized by these beautiful little umbrella-like plants. Two or three other, less conspicuous species may be encountered in Florida.

119b Not as in 119a...120

120a Thallus under 2 cm. tall, simple. Fig. 159......*Neomeris annulata*

Fig. 159. *Neomeris annulata* Dickie

The upper portion of an actively growing specimen, × 8. Although the individual plants are small they often grow in large numbers on bits of coral and shell along the Florida coast where they are conspicuous because of the bright green tips of the white, calcified plants.

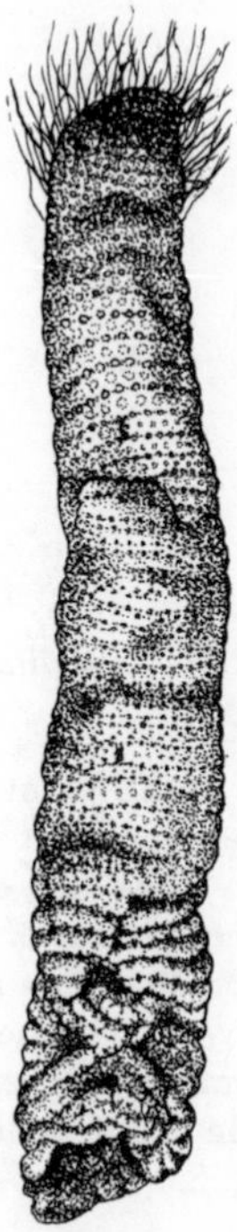

120b Thallus larger, branched..............121

Figure 159

121a Thallus irregularly to dichotomously branched..............123

121b Thallus consisting of a simple stalk with a terminal tuft of branches 122

122a Terminal tuft consisting of free filaments. Fig. 160.....*Penicillus*

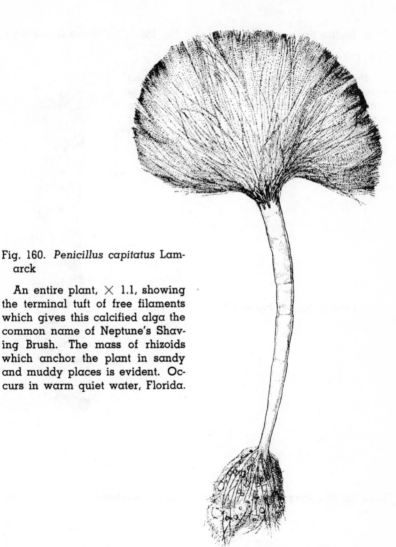

Fig. 160. *Penicillus capitatus* Lamarck

An entire plant, × 1.1, showing the terminal tuft of free filaments which gives this calcified alga the common name of Neptune's Shaving Brush. The mass of rhizoids which anchor the plant in sandy and muddy places is evident. Occurs in warm quiet water, Florida.

Figure 160

122b Terminal tuft consisting of filaments which are united, at least in part, into small blades. Fig. 161.................*Rhipocephalus*

Fig. 161. *Rhipocephalus phoenix* (Solander) Kützing

An entire plant, × 1.2.

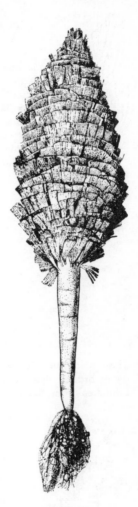

Figure 161

There are only two species of this interesting genus which is confined to the West Indian region. Both of them occur in southern Florida in the same kinds of sandy habitats occupied by *Penicillus* and *Udotea*. *R. phoenix* is the more abundant and widespread of the two, and it is for its recognition that the union of the filaments of the terminal tuft into small, narrow, flabellate blades is pointed out in the key. In the other species, *R. oblongus*, these filaments are united only in youth, and older, well developed specimens may rather closely resemble *Penicillus capitatus*. Inasmuch as all of these plants may be found growing together, one should attempt to make series of specimens of all sizes and ages in order, by comparison, to distinguish them clearly. One will note that small plants of *R. oblongatus* often have funnel-shaped or markedly elongate heads. Also, if one looks closely for specimens showing the partial or evanescent union of the filaments of the head, he will have found the distinguishing character of the genus *Rhipocephalus*.

123

123a **Thallus firm to soft, but not mucilaginous; cortex more compact than the medulla and variously modified. Fig. 162....** *Galaxaura*

Fig. 162. *Galaxaura oblongata* (Solander) Lamouroux

A small upper part of a plant, $\times$ 1.2. This is one of several species found in the tropical waters of Florida. Most of the species are cylindrical, but *G. marginata* (Solander) Lamouroux is flat. Most of the species show some indication of banding, whether smooth like *G. oblongata* or covered with assimilative filaments (superficial hairs) like *G. subverticillata* Kjellman.

Figure 162

123b **Thallus soft, usually somewhat mucilaginous, at least in the vicinity of branch tips; cortex formed of branched lateral fascicles of branches from the medullary filaments. Fig. 163........** *Liagora*

Fig. 163. *Liagora ceranoides* Lamouroux

A small upper part of a plant showing the irregularly dichotomous branching habit, $\times$ 1.3. This is one of several species which may be found in the tropical waters of Florida. Some of them become quite heavily calcified so that lower parts are rigid, although the tips may remain soft. The genus is represented on our Pacific Coast by a single species, *G. californica* Zeh, which is common at Catalina Island, near Los Angeles.

Figure 163

124

**124a Main cell attached by several small rhizoidal cells at the base.
Fig. 164.....................................*Valonia ventricosa***

Fig. 164. *Valonia ventricosa* J. Agardh

Fig. 164. *Valonia ventricosa* J. Agardh

Habit of a small plant showing the basal rhizoidal organs attached to a sand grain, and two very young thalli attached to the base, × 4. Common in some quiet water habitats in southern Florida. This is a famous plant on account of the size to which a single cell may grow (to 3.5 cm.) and the physiological experiments which have been conducted upon it.

Figure 164

**124b Main cell attached to crustose corallines by a penetrating peg.
Fig. 165.....................................*Halicystis ovalis***

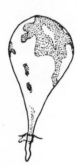

Fig. 165. *Halicystis ovalis* (Lyngbye) Areschoug

Habit of a plant showing the characteristic, penetrating, basal peg, × 3.2. Epiphytic on crustose corallines at lowest tide levels from southern California northward.

Figure 165

125a Thallus with a midrib, median stipe, and (or) other veins....126

125b Thallus without a midrib, median stripe or veins.............143

126a Thallus simple or branched only at the base................127

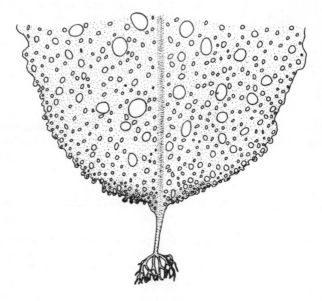

Figure 166

Fig. 166. *Agarum cribrosum* (Mertens) Bory

The lower part of a small plant showing the holdfast, midrib, and perforations of the blade, $\times$ 0.5. This is a cold water plant occurring in northern New England and also in the Puget Sound region of our north Pacific Coast. It is normally found in deep water, but dwarfed examples may be encountered intertidally. Another species, *A. fimbriatum* Harvey, with fewer and less conspicuous perforations and flattened rather than cylindrical stipe occurs abundantly in the lower Puget Sound and sparingly in deep water along the southern California coast.

128b Blade not perforated. Fig. 167............*Pleurophycus gardneri*

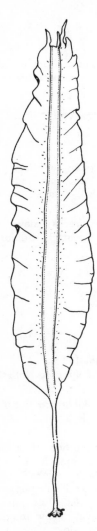

Figure 167

Fig. 167. *Pleurophycus gardneri* Setchell & Saunders

An entire plant to show the unbranched habit, the broad, flat "midrib," and ruffled margins of the blade, × 0.1.

Although this species is reported in the literature from Yakutat Bay, Alaska to as far south as the mouth of Coos Bay, Oregon, it may well extend on down the coast to California. Its wide separation from *Laminaria* in this key, because of its prominent, broad "midrib," or fold, is quite artificial, for it seemingly is closely related to that genus. This solitary member of the genus *Pleurophycus* was discovered at the end of the last century almost simultaneously by two different workers, one at Whidbey Island, Washington, the other at Yakutat Bay, Alaska. In Washington it was growing just below low water mark in places much exposed to the fury of the waves, while in Alaska it appeared abundantly in drift.

Pleurophycus apparently comes into reproductive condition only once and then dies. The zoosporangial sori are borne in narrow areas on both surfaces of the broad "midrib."

129a Thallus simple, or lobed and deeply divided or lacerated; holdfast not dichotomous.....................................130

129b Thallus consisting of several strap-shaped blades from a dichotomously branched holdfast. Fig. 168..*Dictyoneurum californicum*

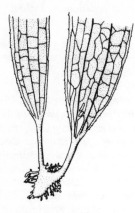

Fig. 168. *Dictyoneurum californicum* Ruprecht

Basal part of a plant to show the dichotomous holdfast and the reticulate venation of the ligulate blades, $\times$ 0.5.

Frequent on surfy rocks along the Pacific Coast from central California northward.

Figure 168

130a Blades reddish, with a network of veins. Fig. 169.............
....*Polyneura latissima*

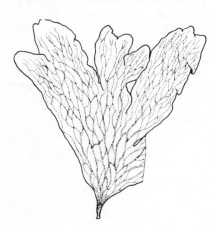

Fig. 169. *Polyneura 'latissima* (Harvey) Kylin

A lower portion of a plant showing the small holdfast, the deeply divided, lobed blade and the network of anastomosing veins, $\times$ 0.6. This plant occurs on rocks at low intertidal levels and below along virtually the entire Pacific Coast. In southern California it is infratidal and will be encountered only in drift or by dredging.

Figure 169

130b Blades brownish, with five percurrent ribs. Fig. 170 . . . .
. . . . *Costaria costata*

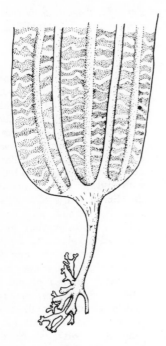

Figure 170

Fig. 170. *Costaria costata* (Turner) Saunders

The lower part of a relatively small plant showing the holdfast of branched hapteres, the simple stipe and the five prominent ribs of the blade, three on one side and two on the other, $\times$ 0.7. This species is variable in size and shape. It may reach a height of two meters and a breadth of 30 cm., the blade being either ovate or narrowly lanceolate. It may be found on rocks, wood, or other large algae in the lower intertidal and upper infratidal regions along the whole Pacific Coast from the Bering Sea to southern California. In the southernmost part of the range, however, plants are usually confined to moderately deep water. The mature blades fruit from midsummer until late in the fall, the sporangial sori largely covering the bullate, or blistered portions of the surface.

There has long been a difference of opinion among phychologists as to the number of species of *Costaria* that should be recognized. The members of the genus as they are now known are confined to the North Pacific Ocean. Four species and one variety have been referred to *Costaria* on our North American Coast from one time to another, but Setchell and Gardner in their 1925 monograph concluded that only one exceedingly variable species, namely, *C. costata*, is present in this area. More recently the Japanese have reached the same conclusion for their plants on the western side of the North Pacific.

129

131a Thallus with a coarse, dichotomously branched stipe, but the slender, ligulate blades simple. Fig. 171....*Lessoniopsis littoralis*

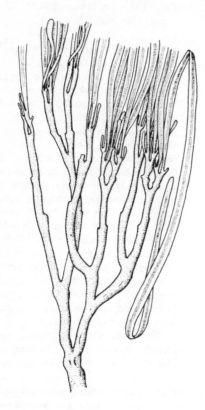

Figure 171

Fig. 171. *Lessoniopsis littoralis* (Farlow & Setchell, ex Tilden) Reinke

The lower part of a young plant showing the coarse, forked stipe and ligulate blades, one of them intact, × 0.52. Grows on rocks at low tide level subject to heavy surf, from central California northward. The ligulate blades with midribs are always sterile. Small fertile blades (sporophylls) without midribs develop year after year in lateral pairs below the ligulate blades. This species and *Postelsia palmaeformis* are among the most striking of our Pacific cumatophytes, or "surf-loving plants" for there appears to be no limit to the amount of wave shock they can withstand. *Lessoniopsis* grows at somewhat lower levels than *Postelsia*, apparently having less resistance to desiccation which may occasionally be prolonged during calm weather coincident with low tides.

134a Blades with a distinct, regular row of cryptostomata (showing as small tufts of hairs) on either side of the midrib. Fig. 172. . . . . .
. . . . *Hesperophycus harveyanus*

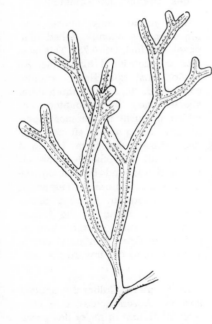

Figure 172

Fig. 172. *Hesperophycus harveyanus* (Decaisne) Setchell & Gardner

Part of a vegetative plant to show the midrib and the rows of cryptostomata on either side, × 1.0. This is a common plant on the exposed tops of upper intertidal rocks along the coast of California to as far north as Monterey Bay. It is easily obtained at almost any low tide, for it grows only a few feet below highest water levels and is markedly resistant to desiccation. In southern California it is often mistaken for a species of the closely related genus *Fucus*, but inasmuch as *Fucus* is confined on our Pacific Coast to the region north of Point Conception, California, *Hesperophycus* cannot be confused with it to the south. A distictive and readily recognizable character is the presence on most plants of abundant, extruded paraphyses from the rows of cryptostomata. These are usually whitish in color and quite conspicuous.

135a Holdfast stupose (felted, fibrous). Fig. 173..........*Dictyopteris*

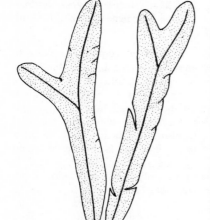

Figure 173

Fig. 173. *Dictyopteris polypodioides* (Desfontaine) Lamouroux

Two young blades shown arising from the spongy, felted (stupose) holdfast, $\times$ 0.75. This species is occasional along the Atlantic Coast from North Carolina southward. In Florida three other species may be encountered of which *D. justii* is the most spectacular, being up to 40 cm. high and with blades from 1½ to 4 cm. broad. The other two species, *D. delicatula* and *D. plagiogramma*, are smaller and distinguished by the irregular, tangled, dichotomous branching of the former and the irregular, alternate branching of the latter with small lateral veins leading out toward the margins.

In southern California another species, *D. zonarioides*, is a common inhabitant of rocky tide pools, especially those which are somewhat sheltered and well insolated at low tide. In such habitats it may be a luxuriant and dominant member of the vegetation which cannot help but attract attention when sunlight brings out the irridescent highlights of its fronds.

135b Holdfast solid, not stupose. Fig. 174.............*Fucus* **(in part)**

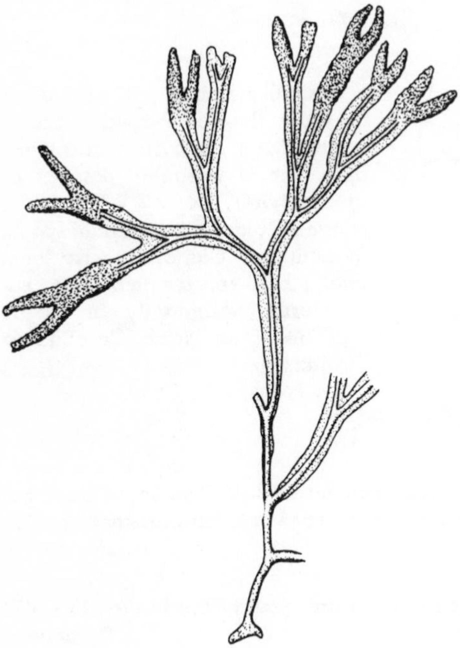

Fig. 174. *Fucus edentatus* De
la Pylaie

A fertile plant of a small form of the species from central Oregon showing the simple, solid holdfast and t h e swollen reproductive parts (receptacles) at the ends of the blades, × 0.6.

The genus *Fucus* is one of the most prevalent intertidal algae in the cooler waters of our coasts. From central California northward one or more species may be found at almost any station, while the same is true on the Atlantic Coast to the north of New Jersey. *F. edentatus* occurs widely on both coasts. Some species of *Fucus* have inflated vesicles and may be noted elsewhere in this key (See Step 100a).

Figure 174

It is to this genus that many of the so-called "rock weeds" belong which are of such economic importance to the people of north Atlantic shores. It is these plants which first furnished the burned ash or "kelp" for the manufacture of soda used in glass and pottery making in 17th century France. The value of such "rock weeds" as fertilizer has been known and exploited for centuries, and in some areas of western Europe they have been importantly used for stock feed.

133

136a Ultimate thallus parts fan-shaped, usually with some concentric hair lines. Fig. 175 .... *Zonaria*

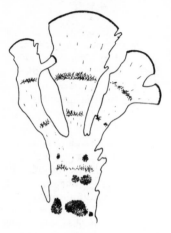

Figure 175

Fig. 175. *Zonaria farlowii* Setchell & Gardner

A small terminal part of a plant to show the fan-shaped ultimate thallus parts, the curved hair lines, and several irregular patches of aplanospores, $\times$ 2.7. This is a common plant of intertidal pools in southern California. At least two other species may be encountered abundantly in some localities from North Carolina to Florida.

136b Not as above, the whole thallus often flabellate in outline, but not the individual ultimate parts; concentric lines absent 137

137a Tetrasporangial sori occurring on any part of the blade. Fig. 176. .... *Hymenena*

Fig. 176. *Hymenena flabelligera* (J. Agardh) Kylin

A small, upper portion of a fertile, asexual plant showing the system of delicate veins and a number of elongate tetrasporangial sori, $\times$ 1. This is one of several species which occur at lowest intertidal levels and below along the Pacific Coast from central California to Puget Sound.

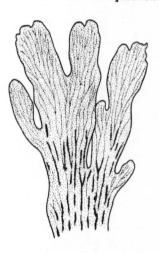

Figure 176

137b Tetrasporangial sori restricted to the margins of the blades and
(or) to proliferous outgrowths along the margins............138

138a Blades densely fringed with small, flat or ruffled, overlapping
marginal outgrowths to which the tetrasporangia are restricted.
Fig. 177...........................*Botryoglossum farlowianum*

Figure 177

Fig. 177. *Botryoglossum farlowianum*
(J. Agardh) G. DeToni

A small terminal portion of a blade
showing the system of delicate veins
and the development of the dense,
marginal fringe of small, overlapping
outgrowths, × 1. This is a frequent
species on lowest intertidal rocks or
below along the entire Pacific Coast
except in southernmost California
where the plant is found at moderate
infratidal depths. It is the only member of the genus recognized in our
area, but, inasmuch as *Botryoglossum*
was founded upon a species from
South Africa, there is some question
about the true generic identity of the
Pacific American plants. Our plant
is clearly of very close relationship
with *Cryptopleura*, and separated
rather unconvincingly. Fortunately, it
can be recognized specifically by the characters of the marginal outgrowths mentioned in the key, and also by its large size (to 35 cm.
tall) and broad upper blade segments (to 2 cm.).

138b Blades not so densely fringed with outgrowths, or these at least not densely crowded and strongly overlapping. Fig. 178......
.... *Cryptopleura*

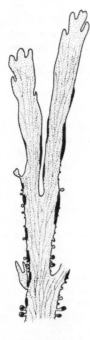

Fig. 178. *Cryptopleura violacea* (J. Agardh) Kylin

A small terminal portion of a fertile asexua. plant showing the system of delicate veins, the scattered small marginal outgrowths, and a number of linear, marginal tetrasporangial sori as well as small elliptical ones in some of the marginal outgrowths, $\times$ 0.9. This is the most common and widespread member of this Pacific genus, occurring along the entire coast. About seven other species may be found more or less locally along California shores.

Figure 178

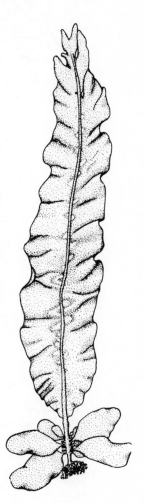

Fig. 179. *Alaria marginata* Postels & Ruprecht

An entire small plant with some of the lower pinnate blades (sporophylls) removed, × 0.12. This species of northern California and southern Oregon is one of several kinds which occur in the colder waters of both coasts. The alarias reach their richest development along the Alaska Coast, but four species occur from central California northward and five others on the Atlantic shores of northern Massachusetts and Maine. An Alaskan species, *A. fistulosa* is one of our most massive giant kelps, reaching lengths of more than 75 feet.

Figure 179

137

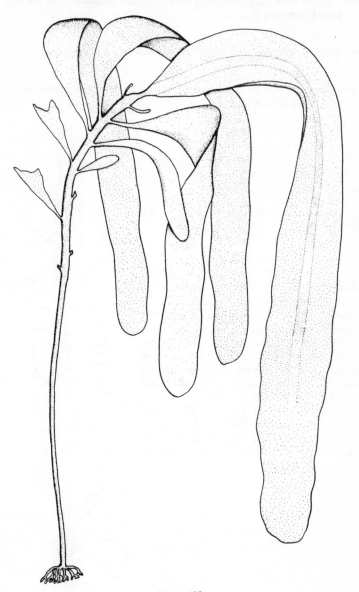

Figure 180

140b Lateral and terminal blades of similar shape and usually of similar size. Fig. 180 . . . . *Pterygophora californica*

Fig. 180. *Pterygophora californica* Ruprecht

An entire small intertidal plant, × 0.25. Occurs along the entire Pacific Coast, mostly in infratidal beds where the plants reach a large size of 8 feet or more in length. Intertidal specimens are smaller, more scattered, and are absent in the southern part of the range although the plant may commonly be found in driftweed. This species is a perennial. Each winter the sporophylls, of which as many as 12 to 18 may mature in a season, disintegrate to leave scars on the stipe. Some plants studied in northern Washington were estimated to be thirteen years old from counts of the number of scars on the stipe.

141a Thallus brownish; growth trichothallic. (This must be observed in young, growing tips.) Fig. 181 . . . . *Desmarestia* (in part)

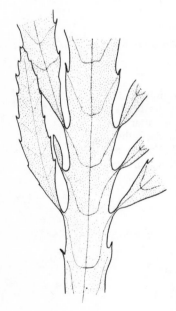

Fig. 181. *Desmarestia munda* Setchell & Gardner

A small mid-portion of a plant showing the very slender, opposite veins and opposite branches characteristic of the flat, ligulate members of this genus, × 0.6.

Several species occur more or less widely along the Pacific Coast. The only flattened Atlantic species, *D. aculeata* (Linnaeus) Lamouroux, is very narrow and alternately branched, occurring north of New Jersey. Cylindrical species of *Desmarestia* are treated under step 24a of this key.

Species of this genus are exceedingly acid in character (pH 1.0) and will damage other algae placed in contact with them in field collections.

Figure 181

142a **Thallus provided with frequent small, hook-shaped branches; midrib absent; microscopic veins present. Fig. 182**...............
....*Acrosorium uncinatum*

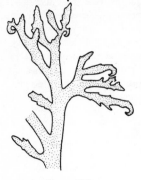

Fig. 182. *Acrosorium uncinatum* (Turner) Kylin

Part of a plant bearing several of the characteristic hooked branches, $\times$ 1.3. The delicate veins, which must be seen with a lens, are not indicated in the figure.

This is a common, epiphytic plant of southern California.

Figure 182

142b **Thallus without hook-shaped branches; midrib present, at least in lower parts. Fig. 183**..............................*Nienburgia*

Fig. 183. *Nienburgia andersoniana* (J. Agardh) Kylin

A small upper branch showing the midrib in lower parts and the dentate margins of the blade, $\times$ 1.2. Common at low intertidal levels, often in grottos, under overhanging rocks, or under other algae and surf-grass, from southern California to Oregon. Another species, *N. borealis* Kylin, occurs in Puget Sound.

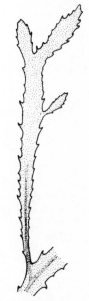

Figure 183

143a Blade saucer-shaped, attached near the center to a short stipe. Fig. 184..*Constantinea*

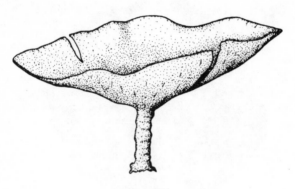

Figure 184

Fig. 184. *Constantinea simplex* Setchell

An entire small plant, $\times$ 1.1. This is one of the most peculiarly shaped of our Pacific Coast red algae. It occurs at low tide level from central California to Washington. Another species inhabits the Puget Sound region of Washington.

143b Blade not saucer-shaped.................................144

144a Thallus consisting of a single sessile or stipitate, fan-shaped primary blade (sometimes 2 or 3) which may be simple, divided or lacerate; color brown or greenish..........................145

144b Thallus simple or variously branched; if simple and broadly expanded, at least not fan-shaped; if branched and dichotomous or subdichotomous, any resulting fan-like form arises from the branching; color brownish, greenish or reddish....................147

145a Thallus usually under 20 cm. tall, greenish, spongy. Fig. 185....
....*Avrainvillea*

Figure 185

Fig. 185. *Avrainvillea* sp.

An entire plant to show the flabellate form of the spongy thallus,
× 1. Several species may be found in quiet, shallow water on sandy
or muddy bottoms in southern Florida. They are not particularly
abundant, nor are the dark, often silt covered blades attractive. The
spongy thallus is made up of branched, interlaced filaments which
provide certain diagnostic characters for distinguishing species.

145b Thallus large, usually over 20 cm. tall, coarse, brown, firm....146

146a Thallus sessile. Fig. 186 . . . . *Hedophyllum*

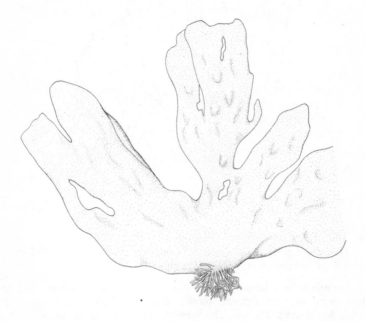

Figure 186

Fig. 186. *Hedophyllum sessile* (C. Agardh) Setchell

A plant of moderate size showing the sessile, irregularly divided, fan-shaped blade, × 0.32.

This genus is represented by two species occurring along the colder, northern portions of our Pacific Coast all the way to the Bering Sea. *H. sessile* extends as far south as central California.

146b Thallus stipitate. Fig. 187.................*Laminaria* (in part)

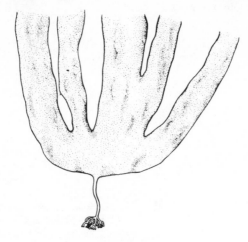

Figure 187

Fig. 187. *Laminaria digitata* (Linnaeus) Edmonson

The lower part of a plant showing the holdfast, stipe and deeply divided or lacerated, fan-shaped blade, × 0.32.

Laminaria is a large genus of medium to small size kelps of which some have narrow, ligulate blades and some, like *L. digitata*, have broad, fan-shaped blades. The former will be encountered a little farther along in this key. All of the species of *Laminaria* are characteristic of cool to cold waters. On the central and northern parts of the Pacific Coast they may be found in almost any rocky area, but in southern California are confined to infratidal areas of cold, upwelling water. On the Atlantic Coast they are largely confined to the cold waters north of Cape Cod and are best developed at some depth below low tide level. About fifteen species may be found in the United States. (See other comments at step 150b.)

147a Plants essentially simple, consisting of one or more entire or lobed blades; branching mainly restricted to basal region although sometimes the blades proliferous from the flattened surfaces *(Caulerpa)*, or from the margins *(Gigartina; Grateloupia)*...............148

147b Plants branched in upper parts.............................160

148a Plants with sand-penetrating rhizoids and erect blades from creeping, stoloniferous parts. Fig. 188............ *Caulerpa prolifera*

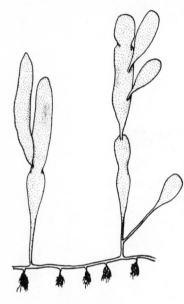

Fig. 188. *Caulerpa prolifera* (Forskal) Lamouroux

Part of a plant to show the creeping, stolon part with sand-penetrating rhizoids, and the flat, erect blades with proliferous branches, ✕ 0.6. Grows in quiet waters of south and west Florida. Other species of this genus of varied morphology are treated elsewhere in this key.

Figure 188

148b Holdfasts simple and discoid, or of coarse hapteres, without penetrating rhizoids 149

149a Blades from a prominent stipe several centimeters long......150

149b Blades estipitate, or from a very short stipe.................151

150a Thallus with a disc-shaped holdfast. Fig. 189 ....
.... *Phyllaria dermatodea*

Fig. 189. *Phyllaria dermatodea* (De la Pylaie) Le
Jolis

The lower part of a plant showing the simple,
discoid holdfast and the entire, ligulate blade,
$\times$ 0.22.

Found on surfy rocks at lowest tide levels and
below, from northern Massachusetts northward.

The form of the blade is like that of several
species of *Laminaria*, especially some of the narrow Pacific Coast forms.

Figure 189

150b Thallus with a holdfast of branched hapteres
.... *Laminaria* (in part)

Except for the type of holdfast, which is like
that in Fig. 187, the several species of *Laminaria*
which key out here are of the ligulate, non-flabel-
late form shown in Fig. 189 for *Phyllaria*. Such
forms are represented on the Atlantic Coast by
Laminaria agardhii Kjellman (from New Jersey to
Cape Cod) and by *L. faeroensis* Börgesen (Maine).
Several Pacific species are of this narrow form,
at least in young stages, but one will encounter
on either coast a range of variation among the
species extending from the narrow, ligulate blade
to the broadly cordate or flabellate and lacerate
blade of Fig. 187.

151a Surface and margins of blade covered with small, wart-like or tooth-like papil. Fig. 190...................*Gigartina* (in part)

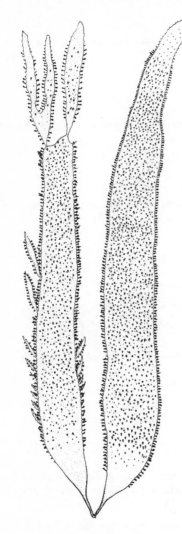

Fig. 190. *Gigartina harveyana* (Kützing) Setchell & Gardner

A maturing cystocarpic plant, $\times$ 0.8. This is a common one of several simple, flat, ligulate to broadly complanate species of this genus on the Pacific Coast. It occurs in California and Oregon. One or more species of this general form may be expected to occur at low levels on most any exposed, rocky shore along the Pacific. Many of the best specimens may be found in drift where their large, conspicuous, reddish blades are sure to attract attention. The characteristic wart-like outgrowths on the blade surfaces provide for an easy means of identification so that the student of Pacific seaweeds quickly becomes familiar with the broad forms of this genus. There are other members of *Gigartina*, however, of very different form, and it is these smaller, much branched subcylindrical or compressed species which usually puzzle the beginner. Some important examples of these other forms of *Gigartina* are treated under steps 168a and 187a.

Figure 190

147

151b Surface of blades smooth..................................152

152a Thallus dark brown or yellowish-brown (as opposed to reddish, purplish or greenish)..................................153

152b Thallus reddish, purplish, or sometimes greenish, but not brown or yellowish-brown..................................154

153a Thallus several layers of cells thick, the medullary cells very different, especially in size, from the surface cells. Fig. 191....... ....*Ilea (Petalonia) fascia*

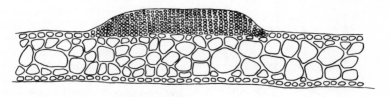

Figure 191

Fig. 191. *Ilea fascia* (Müller) Fries

Part of a transection of a blade showing the difference in size between the medullary cells and the surface cells. The vertical rows of small cells represent gametangia, × 150.

This is a common species along practically the entire Pacific and Atlantic coasts. Its gross appearance is essentially like that shown for *Punctaria* in Fig. 193, but its structure is quite distinct from that genus. In southern California it may be confused with *Endarachne binghamiae* J. Agardh which is almost identical in external appearance. Again, however, a transection readily distinguishes the two, for *Endarachne* has a medulla of intertwined filaments.

153b Thallus thin, of few cell layers, the surface cells little different from those of the inner layers. Fig. 192, 193 ....*Punctaria*

Fig. 192. *Punctaria* sp.

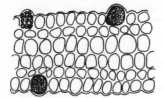

Part of a transection of a blade showing the relatively uniform cell structure compared to *Ilea*, $\times$ 125. A gametangium and two (?) sporangia are shown.

Figure 192

Fig. 193. *Punctaria plantaginea* (Roth) Greville

An entire young plant, $\times$ 0.5. This species, and the somewhat more slender and delicate *P. latifolia* Greville, occur on stones or on algae and *Zostera* from New Jersey northward. On the Pacific Coast four species occur between central California and Puget Sound, Washington, but they are all of infrequent or geographically restricted occurrence.

Figure 193

149

154a Blades with proliferations from the margins. Fig. 194
....*Grateloupia* (in part)

Fig. 194. *Grateloupia schizophylla* Kützing

A single blade of a young plant, × 0.48.
This is a common species along the entire
Pacific Coast, but its blades may be either
entire or proliferous, so that it may key out
under step 158a. Plants may reach a length
of three feet or more.

The genus contains species of varied size
and morphology, some of local distribution and
some of very wide distribution. Abundantly
branched species like G. *filicina* key out at
step 188b, while broad, simple forms like G.
maxima key out at step 158a.

Figure 194

154b Blades without proliferations from the margins..............155

155a Cortex with gland cells. Fig. 195..........*Schizymenia pacifica*

Fig. 195. *Schizymenia pacifica* (Kylin) Kylin

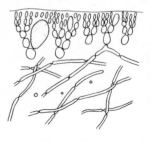

Figure 195

Part of a transection of a blade to show
the gland cells of the cortex and the slender, interlaced filaments of the medulla,
× 224. This species is a frequent, broad,
membranous red alga along the entire
Pacific Coast. Its simple, or lobed, short-
stipitate blades do not show any external
characters satisfactory to distinguish the
plant from other similar membranous algae such as *Halymenia, Cryptonemia, Grateloupia, Rhodoglossum*, etc., and it will be
found most practical to use the presence
of the usually conspicuous large gland
cells for its recognition.

156a Transection showing many of the medullary filaments running from cortex to cortex and more or less perpendicular to the surface of the blade. Figs. 196, 197....................*Halymenia*

Fig. 196. *Halymenia* sp.

Part of a transection of a tetrasporangial blade showing the medullary filaments running from cortex to cortex, × 250.

Figure 196

Fig. 197. *Halymenia gelinaria* Collins & Howe

Habit of a small plant, × 0.5. This is one of several species which occur in infratidal waters from North Carolina to Florida and which are quite often encountered in beach drift. All are broad, rather thin plants of slippery texture. One or more species may also be found in drift along the California coast. Of these, *H. californica* Smith & Hollenberg may be recognized by its cross section and broadly falcate (sickle-shaped) blades.

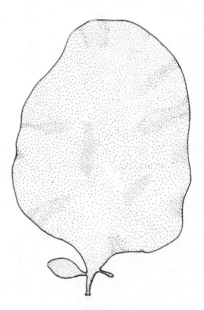

Figure 197

156b Transection showing few or no medullary filaments running from cortex to cortex and perpendicular to the blade surface......157

157a Tetrasporangia borne individually in the cortical tissue of the blade, not touching each other or occurring in masses. Fig. 198..
....**158**

Figure 198

Fig. 198. *Cryptonemia obovata* J. Agardh

Part of a transection of a tetrasporic blade showing an individual tetrasporangium in the cortex, × 520. One of the characteristic medullary filaments with highly refractive contents is shown in cross section.

157b Tetrasporangia borne in masses embedded deeply in the blade. Fig. 199 ....**159**

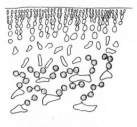

Figure 199

Fig. 199. Iridophycus sp.

Part of a transection of a young tetrasporic blade to show the origin of the sporangia (undivided) among the medullary filaments well inside of the cortex (Modified after Kylin).

158a Cortex composed of small cells arranged more or less clearly in anticlinal rows; medulla without refractive filaments. Fig. 200...
....*Grateloupia* (in part)

Fig. 200. *Grateloupia maxima* (Gardner) Kylin

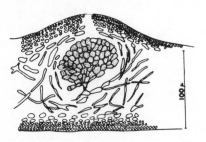

Figure 200

Transection of a blade through a cystocarp showing cortical cell rows, especially on lower surface, × 200.

This is one of the broad species with entire blades which may be found along the California coast. Nonproliferous spécimens of *G. schizophylla* key out here (see Fig. 194). Such broad, membranous species of *Grateloupia* do not occur along the Atlantic Coast

158b Cortex composed of cells usually showing little or no arrangement in anticlinal rows; medulla with refractive filaments. Figs. 198, 201 .... *Cryptonemia*

Fig. 201. *Cryptonemia obovata*
J. Agardh

Habit of a young plant, × 0.36. This is one of two species which may be encountered frequently in beach drift along the Pacific Coast. Unlike *Grateloupia* or *Halymenia*, the blades are not slippery in texture, but rather firm and crisp. The blades are reduced at the base to a very slender, short stipe.

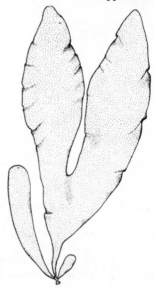

Figure 201

159a Tetrasporangia developing between the medullary filaments. Figs. 199, 202 .... *Iridophycus*

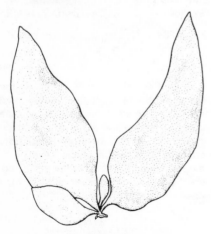

Figure 202

Fig. 202. *Iridophycus flaccidum* Setchell & Gardner

Habit of a young plant, × 0.32. This is a common species of a genus of several species occurring from central California northward. *Iridophycus* grows mostly at low intertidal levels, and sometimes in great abundance. *I. flaccidum* and at least one other species have been harvested commercially in Oregon and northern California for the production of the phycocolloid *Iridophycin* used in stabilizing chocolate milk. As much as 400 pounds have been collected by one man at a single low tide.

159b Tetrasporangia developing from the innermost cortical cells. Fig. 203.....................................*Rhodoglossum* (in part)

Figure 203

Fig. 203. *Rhodoglossum* sp.

Part of a transection of a tetrasporic blade to show the origin of the tetrasporangia (undivided) from the inner cortical cells (redrawn from Kylin).

Several species of *Rhodoglossum* occur along the Pacific coast which are similar in habit to species of *Iridophycus* (See Fig. 202). These unbranched forms with entire blades will be somewhat difficult for the student to recognize until some experience is gained with them. There are only four species, however, all confined to California except one from Puget Sound. They usually will be less abundant than the species of *Iridophycus*, and, apart from the tetrasporangial character pointed out above, they may be distinguished in another way. *Iridophycus* plants after drying will ordinarily disintegrate when soaked up in fresh water, while specimens of *Rhodoglossum* will not respond in this way.

Note that our commonest species of *Rhodoglossum*, *R. affine*, is dichotomously branched and appears at step 170b in the key.

160a Erect blades pectinately branched from a creeping stolon with sand-penetrating rhizoids. Fig. 204...........*Caulerpa crassifolia*

Figure 204

Fig. 204. *Caulerpa crassifolia* (C. Agardh) J. Agardh

A portion of a plant to show the erect, pectinate, flattened blades and sand-penetrating rhizoids from the creeping stolon, × 0.7. This common species of Florida keys out apart from other species of the genus because of the flattened character of the branched, erect parts. Other species will be noted under steps 59a and 148a.

160b Not as above; without sand-penetrating rhizoids from a stoloniferous base..161

161a Ligulate blades borne in a drooping bunch from the apex of a stiffly erect, heavy stipe...................................162

161b Not as above; blades not borne in a drooping bunch.........163

162a Apex of stipe strongly forked. Fig. 205..........*Eisenia arborea*

Fig. 205. *Eisenia arborea*
  Areschoug

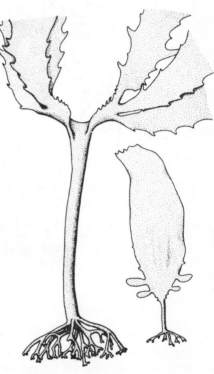

A. A young plant showing the beginning of erosion of the apex of the primary blade and the development of the lateral blades from the meristematic area at the base of the primary blade, × 0.32.

B. The lower part of an older plant showing how the stipe has elongated and increased in thickness while the primary blade has eroded away completely to its base to produce an artificial forking at which the lateral blades arise on either side of the base of the old primary blade, × 0.32.

Figure 205

This is a common plant of low intertidal levels and below on rocky shores of southern California. It is sometimes mistaken for *Postelsia* because of its habit, but the ranges of these two plants do not overlap. *Eisenia* is one of the principal components of the "submarine gardens" of Catalina Island, California.

155

162b Apex of stipe not forked. Fig. 206........*Postelsia palmaeformis*

Figure 206

Fig. 206. *Postelsia palmaeformis* Ruprecht

Habit of a group of plants from a "grove," $\times$ 0.25. This plant may commonly be observed on the Pacific Coast from central California to Vancouver Island, B. C., but its habitat is such as to make collection of specimens difficult. The "groves" occur on rocks at low intertidal levels in places which are subjected to the full force of the heaviest surf. Many of them are completely inaccessible on outlying rocky ledges, but others may be reached at times of lowest tides in calm weather. The heavy, elastic stipes are exceedingly well adapted to the pounding surf conditions of *Postelsia's* habitat.

163a Thallus branched in the manner of an *Opuntia* cactus, the blades or branches all more or less circular or elliptical in outline. Fig. 207.......................................*Opuntiella californica*

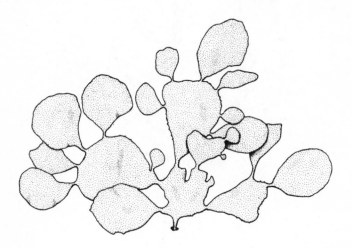

Figure 207

Fig. 207. *Opuntiella californica* (Farlow) Kylin

Habit of an entire plant, × 0.28. Grows on rocks at lowest tide levels and below from central California northward, but usually as isolated thalli. It is more frequently found in beach drift. It should be pointed out that juvenile or poorly developed plants of this species will be difficult to recognize, for the distinctive cactoid form will not necessarily be evident.

163b Not as above; blades or branches not at all circular in shape..164

164a Primary branching of thallus dichotomous or subdichotomous, or subpalmate to produce a flabellate form at least in upper parts.165

164b Primary branching essentially in one plane, but not dichotomous, subdichotomous or subpalmate. (But note dichotomous tendency in Fig. 224)..178

165a Terminal portions of fertile dichotomies swollen and broader than region below. Fig. 208..166

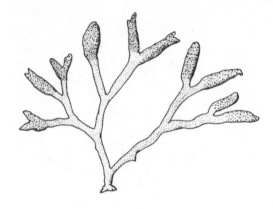

Figure 208

Fig. 208. *Pelvetiopsis limitata* (Setchell) Gardner

Habit of part of a plant, $\times$ 0.7, showing the swollen ends of the branches (receptacles) containing the small, sunken, fertile cavities (conceptacles). This is a common species of middle and high intertidal rocks from central California northward.

Pelvetia fastigiata (J. Agardh) De Toni, which is similar in habit and habitat, but much taller, occurs commonly along the entire California coast to southern Oregon. In southern California it is the only such olive-green, ribless species with swollen branch apices on the high intertidal rocks.

165b Terminal portions of fertile dichotomies about the same width as lower parts, or, if broader, at least not swollen..............167

166a Thalli short, 4-15 cm. tall; macrosporangia (oogonia) with only one functional spore. (See Figs. 208, 209A)...*Pelvetiopsis limitata*

166b Thalli larger, 15-40 cm. tall; macrosporangia (oogonia) with two functional spores. Fig. 209B..................*Pelvetia fastigiata*

Fig. 209.

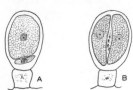

Figure 209

Macrosporangia of two closely related genera: A, *Pelvetiopsis*, and B, *Pelvetia*. These are shown removed from the inner wall of the conceptacle in which each was produced. In the case of *Pelvetiopsis* a single functional spore is seen, the remaining nuclei from the divisions of the macrosporangium being separated off in a non-functional mass below. In *Pelvetia* two functional spores are seen with the extruded nuclei between. Various stages in the development of these macrospores as well as the microspores (antherozoids) may be observed by cutting transections of receptacles bearing maturing conceptacles.

See note regarding *Pelvetia* under Fig. 208.

167a Medulla composed mainly or entirely of large, parenchymatous cells 171

167b Medulla not composed of large parenchymatous cells, but of densely or loosely packed ramified filaments, mostly longitudinally arranged 168

168a Flat surface of branches provided with small, wart-like or spine-like papillae. Fig. 210......................*Gigartina* (in part)

Figure 210

Fig. 210. *Gigartina stellata* Batters

An entire, maturing plant, × 1. This species from the Atlantic Coast, occurring from Rhode Island northward, is illustrated as an example of a rather diversified group of *Gigartina* species which will best key out here. These are all flattened, more or less clearly dichotomously branched f o r m s bearing papillose or spinose outgrowths from the flattened surfaces of the broader blade parts. About half a dozen Pacific Coast species fall within this assemblage, of which *G. cristata* (Setchell) Setchell & Gardner is probably the most widespread. Smith's (1944) illustrations of several California species are helpful to students in learning to recognize these polymorphic gigartinas. The only available monographic treatment is Setchell and Gardner 1933, (Univ. Calif. Publ. Bot. 17 (10):255-340) which contains numerous photographs.

Other species of this genus are treated in this key under steps 151a and 235a.

168b Flat surfaces of branches smooth............................169

169a Thallus normally with determinate secondary pinnate branches from the primary dichotomous branches. Fig. 211.............
....*Zanardinula* (in part)

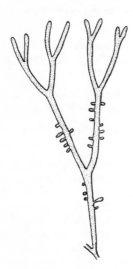

Fig. 211. *Zanardinula cornea* (Okamura) Dawson

A small upper portion of a plant about 20 cm. high to show the dichotomous primary branching and determinate secondary pinnate branchlets, × 1.1. This is a Pacific Coast genus of which one or more of our half dozen species may be found at almost any rocky intertidal station from southern California to Washington. *Z. cornea*, found from central Oregon southward, is one of three species which will key out here because of the dichotomous primary branching. The others will not give the impression of being dichotomous and will key out under step 188a.

Figure 211

169b Thallus normally without determinate secondary pinnate branches
....170

170a Species of Atlantic Coast occurrence. Fig. 212.. *Chondrus crispus*

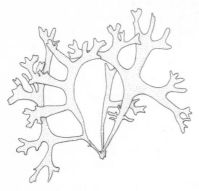

Figure 212

Fig. 212. *Chondrus crispus* (Linnaeus) Stackhouse

A portion of a plant removed from a clump, × 0.8. Although this species may not readily be distinguished from the Pacific *Rhodoglossum affine* except through the study of certain reproductive details, the two need not be confused, for their ranges on opposite coasts do not overlap. *C. crispus* occurs from New Jersey northward and is the famous Irish Moss which has been collected commercially for over a century, especially around Scituate, Massachusetts. It is the source of a phycocolloid called carrageenin which is widely used as a stabilizer in chocolate milk, salad dressings, tooth paste, lotions, syrups, etc. About a million pounds are produced in a year.

170b Species of Pacific Coast occurrence. Fig. 213.................
.. *Rhodoglossum affine*

Figure 213

Fig. 213. *Rhodoglossum affine* (Harvey) Kylin

A portion of a plant removed from a clump, × 0.8. This is the only dichotomous member of *Rhodoglossum* in our territory. It is widespread along the coast from central Oregon southward. In central and southern California it is often dominant in some intertidal, rocky shore areas. It is exceedingly variable in width of thallus parts, in color, and in branch shape, so that many specimens which may be found will not appear to agree with the illustration. The more or less clearly evident dichotomous branching, the filamentous structure and smooth surfaces of the segments will distinguish it.

161

171a Medulla of middle parts of blades composed of a single, uniform layer of large cells. Fig. 214.............................172
171b Medulla composed throughout of more than one layer of large cells, or at least the medullary cells not uniform............173
172a Blades with both medulla and cortex monostromatic throughout. Fig. 214..*Dictyota*

Figure 214

Fig. 214. *Dictyota* sp.

Transection of the margin of a blade showing the monostromatic cortex and monostromatic medulla. In the genus *Pachydictyon* (Fig. 215) the medulla is distromatic at the margins and the cortex of two or more layers.

Dictyota is a warm water genus represented by one common species, *D. flabellata* (Collins) Setchell & Gardner, in southern California, and by several species in Florida. *D. dichotoma* (Hudson) Lamouroux, which extends from North Carolina southward, may be considered the commonest Atlantic species. Although some of the species are quite broad and resemble the figure of *Pachydictyon* (Fig. 215), others are narrow and only 1 to 2 mm. broad. Altogether, about nine species are known from our coasts.

172b Blades with distromatic medulla at the margins and di-polystromatic cortex at the margins. Fig. 215....*Pachydictyon coriaceum*

Fig. 215. *Pachydictyon coriaceum* (Holmes) Okamura

The upper portion of a plant to show the branching habit, × 0.56. This is the only member of this genus in our territory. It is common in southern California and is readily distinguished externally from the similar *Dictyota flabellata* by its coarser texture and usually darker color.

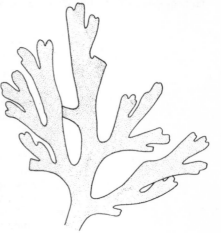

Figure 215

173a Medulla with small cells between the large ones. Fig. 216, 217.
....*Callophyllis*

Fig. 216. *Callophyllis* sp.

Part of a transection of a blade
to show the structure of the medulla in which large and small cells
are intermixed.

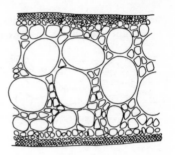

Figure 216

Fig. 217. *Callophyllis
marginifructa* Setchell
& Swezy

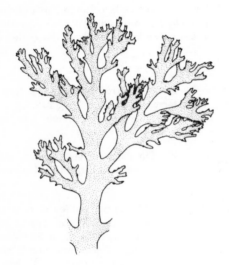

Figure 217

A small upper portion
of a cystocarpic plant
to show the flabellate
branching habit and the
marginal cystocarps, ×
1. This species, occur-
ring from central Ore-
gon to southern Cali-
fornia, is a member of
a common genus on our
Pacific Coast of which
seventeen species may
be collected in drift or
at low intertidal levels.
They are of moderate
size, up to 30 cm., and
vary widely within the
general pattern of dich-
otomo - flabellate form.
Most of them are bright reddish in color and may be made into some
of the most striking and attractive herbarium specimens. In most species the cystocarps are not marginal, but are scattered over the flat
faces of the blades. Until recently it was virtually impossible for the
layman to identify the many species of *Callophyllis,* but now the writer
has published a series of illustrations of all of the Pacific Coast species
with which the student may quite readily identify many of his specimens by the process of matching. (Marine Red Algae of Pacific Mexico.
A. Hancock Pacific Expeditions 17: 1-397. 1953-54.)

173b Medulla composed only of large, parenchymatous cells......174

174a Cortex of 2 to 3 tiers of small cells, not in vertical (anticlinal) rows
except sometimes in tetrasporangial sori. Fig. 218..........175

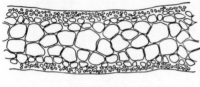

Fig. 218. *Rhodymenia* sp.

Part of a transection of a blade to show the way in which the cortical cells do not present an arrangement in anticlinal rows.

Figure 218

174b Cortex of more than 3 tiers of small cells arranged in anticlinal
rows. (This may be true in *Phyllophora*, step 177b only in older,
thicker parts of blades where secondary growth of the cortex occurs.) 177

175a Cystocarps embedded in the medulla, arranged so as to form a
linear sorus resembling an interrupted midrib. Fig. 219........
....................................*Stenogramme interrupta*

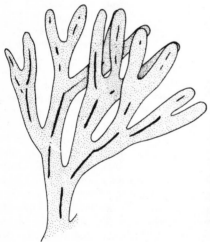

Fig. 219. *Stenogramme interrupta* (C. Agardh) Montagne

An upper portion of a female
plant showing the appearance
of the cystocarps in linear sori,
× 0.8. Tetrasporic plants have
the sporangia in small, irregularly shaped, nemathecial sori
scattered over the flat faces of
the blades. This is the only species of the genus on our coasts.
It may be encountered in drift
or at low intertidal levels along
the entire Pacific shore.

Figure 219

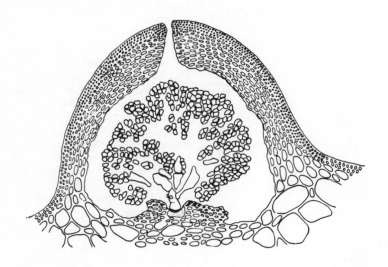

Figure 220

Fig. 220. *Rhodymenia* sp.

A vertical section through a mature cystocarp to show its protruding, dome-like, non-coronate form. The carpospores are produced from a pedicellate gonimoblast. The ostiolar aperture is shown in the top of the pericarp.

Rhodymenia is a world wide genus of some three score species, mostly red in color and found in lower intertidal or in infratidal habitats. The cystocarps are very uniform in structure, and, although infrequently found in some species, are of great aid in identifying the genus. Specific characters are mostly found in the vegetative thallus and in the manner in which the asexual reproductive spores (tetraspores) are produced. The genus is much more richly developed along the Pacific than the Atlantic Coast. Most of the North American species are illustrated in the writer's "Review of the genus *Rhodymenia* with descriptions of new species." (A. Hancock Pacific Expeditions 3:123-181. 1941.)

176a Cystocarps coronate (Fig. 221A); blades subdichotomous and of more or less irregular palmate-flabellate outline. Fig. 221.....
....*Fauchea*

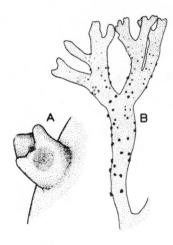

Figure 221

Fig. 221. *Fauchea laciniata* J. Agardh

A. A single coronate cystocarp, × 12. B. A small, upper portion of a large (15 cm.) cystocarpic plant with relatively narrow blade-segments, × 0.8. This species may be encountered frequently at lowest intertidal levels in central and southern California. Plants are often only 5 to 6 cm. wide or high and broadly flabellate. We have only one other species, *F. fryeana* Setchell, in infratidal waters of Puget Sound.

176b Cystocarps not coronate (See Fig. 220); blades subsimple to subdichotomous or regularly dichotomous. Figs. 218, 222.*Rhodymenia*

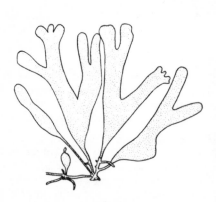

Figure 222

Fig. 222. *Rhodymenia pacifica* Kylin

Part of a plant showing dichotomous branching and the production of stolons at the base, × 0.72. This species and several others of dichotomous form and similar habit occur frequently along the coast of California and southern Oregon. In addition to these there are several species with relatively broad blades and somewhat simpler branching habit. *R. palmata* (Linnaeus) Greville is a broad-bladed plant which is subsimple below and dichotomous or palmately divided above. It occurs along the New England coast as well as in the Puget Sound region of Washington. This is the food-seaweed known as "dulse" which is commercially employed as a thickener in soups, sauces, etc., and is eaten in the raw state or after drying as a salad or vegetable relish.

Our most attractive *Rhodymenia* is *R. pertusa* (Postels & Ruprecht) J. Agardh which occurs from central Oregon northward. It is broad, usually simple, and has many perforations in the blade.

Rhodymenia may often be found without cystocarps, especially the smaller, dichotomous forms occurring intertidally. They have a coarser, more rigid texture than *Fauchea*, however, and lack the very broadly flabellate form.

177a Thallus more or less regularly dichotomous. Fig. 223 . . . .
. . . .*Gymnogongrus* (in part)

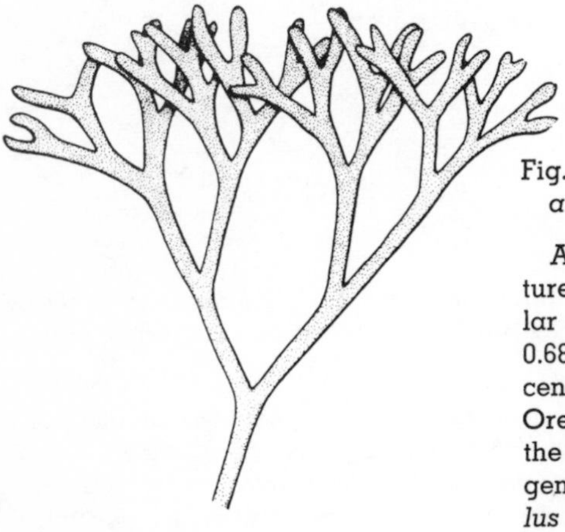

Figure 223

Fig. 223. *Gymnogongrus linearis* (Turner) J. Agardh

An upper portion of a mature plant to show the regular dichotomous branching, × 0.68. This species occurs from central California to central Oregon and is an example of the coarse, broad forms of the genus, of which *G. platyphyllus* Gardner is another occurring in California, and *G. norvegicus* (Gunner) J. Agardh in New England. Beside the slender, cylindrical *G. griffithsiae* treated under step 22a, *G. leptophyllus* J. Agardh is the only slender, narrow species of our territory. It is common along California and Oregon.

177b Thallus irregularly dichotomous or palmate, commonly proliferous. Fig. 224.....................................*Phyllophora*

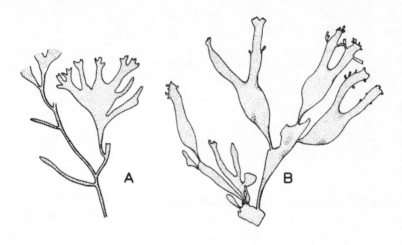

Figure 224

Fig. 224. Portions of *Phyllophora* species: A, *P. membranifolia* (Goodenough & Woodward) J. Agardh; B, *P. brodiaei* (Turner) J. Agardh, both × 1.

These are the two common species of *Phyllophora* of our northeastern coast. Both are characteristic of fairly deep water, usually well below tidal range, but the former comes into lowest tide pools. Both may be found cast up in drift. They are exceedingly variable in form, often highly irregular and proliferous from old, eroded or damaged blades. Three species occur on the California coast, but all are relatively scarce, deep water forms which will not often be encountered except in the dredge or at the hand of a deep diver. The recent rise of the sport of aqua-lunging has, however, brought these plants to some notice, for off Scripps Institution of Oceanography at La Jolla, California where aqua-lung training is conducted, the regularly dichotomous, broad-segmented *Phyllophora clevelandii* is one of the few conspicuous algae encountered in the dim depths below 100 feet.

178a Branching opposite, but the two branches of each opposite pair
not alike. Fig. 225.....................................*Plumaria*
(also known in the literature under the name *Ptilota*)

Figure 225

Fig. 225. *Plumaria filicina* (Farlow) Doty

A single primary lateral branch showing the opposite pairs of
ultimate branchlets and their dissimilarity, × 5. This is one of the
commoner of seven species of this genus which may be encountered
along the Pacific Coast. Although more characteristic of the northern
parts of the coast, three of them extend southward through southern
California. Two other species inhabit Atlantic shores from New Jersey
northward, namely *P. pectinata* (Gunner) Ruprecht and *P. sericea* (Harvey) Ruprecht.

The dissimilarity of ultimate branchlets should be observed in
young parts where the contrasts are usually more pronounced.

Specific characters are to be found in the nature of the margins
of the ultimate branchlets and in the curvature and length of these
branchlets. Thus, in *P. filicina* the branchlets are serrate on both margins, while in *P. densa* they are serrate only on one. Both *P. californica*
and *P. hypnoides* have smooth margined ultimate branchlets, but in the
former they curve upward toward the branch apex while in the latter
they do not. All of these four species are common in California.

178b Branching alternate or irregular, or if opposite, the branches of
opposite pairs essentially alike............................179

179a Ultimate flattened branches, especially of fertile plants, arranged in clusters or fascicles along the major axes which are more or less cylindrical. Fig. 226 .... *Odonthalia*

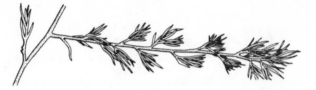

Figure 226

Fig. 226. *Odonthalia floccosa* (Esper) Falkenberg

A small part of a mature plant to show the fasciculate arrangement of the ultimate, short, flattened, acute branchlets, × 1. This is the most widespread of our species of this genus. It ranges from central California northward. In the Puget Sound area of Washington several other local or far northern species occur. They, however, are more flattened, lack the fasciculate arrangement of the branches and are regularly, alternately, distichously branched Some of them show a more or less distinct development of a midrib.

On the Atlantic coast the odonthalias occur north of Maine and outside the scope of this book.

The student should note that this plant is keyed out here under the flattened species on account of the flatness of the ultimate, acute branchlets, but the often cylindrical character of the axes may at times cause one to attempt to key it out among the cylindrical ones in the vicinity of step 33.

179b Ultimate branches not arranged in clusters 180

180a Growth by means of a single apical cell 181

180b Growth apical from a many-celled meristem, not from a single apical cell 186

181a Branches each with an apical pit (See Figs. 18C; 56) in which the growing point is situated. Fig. 227...........*Laurencia* (in part)

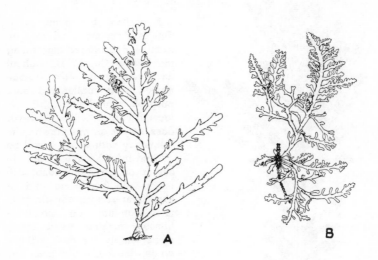

Figure· 227

Fig. 227. Two examples of flattened species of *Laurencia:* A, *L. diego-ensis* Dawson, B, *L. splendens* Hollenberg, both occurring in southern California, × 0.75.

Perhaps the commonest of the flattened laurencias within our territory is *L. spectabilis* Postels & Ruprecht which is similar to *L. diego-ensis*, reaches a height of 20 cm. or more, and occurs from central California northward. No flattened species of this genus seem to occur commonly along any part of the Atlantic coast, although cylindrical species may be found. See step 37b.

181b Branches without an apical pit, although in *Gelidium* sometimes the apex is somewhat indented............................182

171

182a Branching sympodial, the branches of each order unilateral and
pectinate. Fig. 228 .... *Plocamium*

Fig. 228. *Plocamium pacificum*
Kylin

Figure 228

A portion of a plant, × 1.
This is a common and very attractive, delicate red alga along
the Pacific Coast. Throughout
its range it is often accompanied by a smaller and more
purplish colored species, *P. vio-
laceum* Farlow, which, however
does not at all compare in the
frequency with which it will be
noticed by either the casual ob-
server or the professional collector. So handsome and of
such interesting geometric form
is *Plocamium* that one finds
himself making extra specimens simply for their esthetic
value. Indeed, it has been employed in the making of attractive, decorative greeting cards.

Although *P. pacificum* is occasionally epiphytic, it is usually found massed on rocks at
low tide level and below, conspicuous by its rich rose-red
color, and often of moderate size, 10-25 cm. tall. It extends on down
into deeper water, becoming more laxly branched in depths of 20 to
25 feet, and even more brightly colored.

182b Branching monopodial, the branches not unilateral 183

183a Thallus with a large, central axial filament running through the medulla 184

183b Thallus without a large, central axial filament, but with very slender, wire-like rhizoidal filaments packed in longitudinally between the large medullary cells (See Fig. 73).................185

184a The large central axial filament with one or more similar but smaller filaments on either side. Fig. 229................*Pikea*

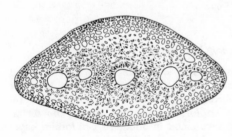

Figure 229

Fig. 229. *Pikea californica* Harvey

Transection of a mature part of a plant to show the aspect of the central axial filament and of the two similar filaments on either side, × 55. This species occurs along the entire Pacific Coast and in southern California is often accompanied by *P. pinnata* Setchell. It is often 10 to 20 cm. tall, and its branching may be described as repeatedly and rather densely and irregularly alternate-pinnate. *P. pinnata* is more regularly pinnate with all the branches in one plane.

184b The large, central axial filament solitary in the medulla. Fig.
230...................................*Leptocladia binghamiae*

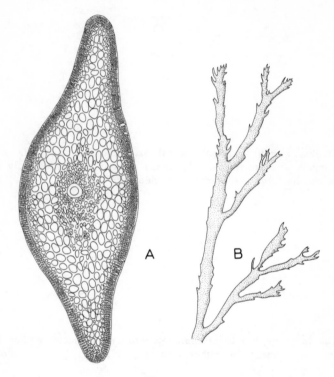

Figure 230

Fig. 230. *Leptocladia binghamiae* J. Agardh

A. Transection of a mature axis to show the single large central
axial filament, $\times$ 46. B. A small upper portion of a plant to show
the very irregularly pinnate branching, $\times$ 2.7. This plant often re-
sembles coarse forms of *Pikea californica*, but may readily be distinguished by the transection. It is common in southern California, especially in drift, and reaches 15 to 30 cm. in height.

It should be pointed out that the genus *Farlowia* is distinguished
from *Leptocladia* only by means of obscure reproductive characters
the examination of which cannot be undertaken by the beginning
student. However, as *Leptocladia* apparently does not occur in central
California and northward, one may assume that plants keying out here
from those regions may well belong to *Farlowia*.

185a Rhizoidal filaments usually aggregated in the central part of the medulla; cystocarps with only one ostiole. Figs. 231, 232.......
....*Pterocladia*

Figure 231

Fig. 231. *Pterocladia caloglossoides* (Howe) Dawson

A small portion of a branch showing two uniostiolate cystocarps, × 16. In *Gelidium*, an ostiole appears on both bulging sides of the cystocarp.

Figure 232

Fig. 232. *Pterocladia pyramidale* (Gardner) Dawson

A very small apical portion of an axis to show the pinnate branching and more or less pyramidal form, × 2.5. This is a common, intertidal plant of southern California, often being a dominant rock-cover alga. It is seasonally variable in form, and old individuals often show much attenuation of the ultimate branches which become dense and somewhat matted. Other species of this genus occur along the California coast, but are small *(P. caloglossoides)* or scarce and local.

175

185b Rhizoidal filaments usually aggregated in the outer portion of the medulla; cystocarps with two ostioles. Fig. 233..............
....*Gelidium* (in part)

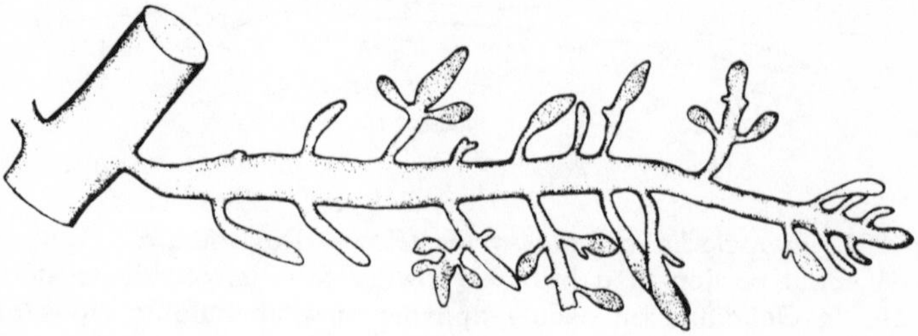

Figure 233

Fig. 233. *Gelidium purpuracens* Gardner

A small portion of a tetrasporangial plant, × 8. This is only one of several `similar, moderate to large species of *Gelidium* inhabiting rocky intertidal and infratidal areas along the Pacific Coast. They are usually strongly compressed in shape, but not very flat. (See also step 45a) *G. cartilagineum* variety *robustum* Gardner, which occurs along the entire coast, but especially in California, is the largest and most abundant. It has been harvested by diver in southern California for the making of agar, especially during World War II when the demand for domestic agar weeds was great and the Japanese supply cut off. Currently, the high cost of harvesting by professional diver in the United States has favored the importation of raw *Gelidium* weed from Japan and from nearby Baja California, Mexico along whose cool shores it grows profusely.

Among the other species of *Gelidium* which may be recognized along the Pacific Coast are the polystichously branched *G. polystichum* from the southern California Channel Islands, and *G. papenfussii* from southern California which is distichous and distinguished by tetrasporangial branchlets with long, slender "stipes." *G. pulchrum* from southern California is a rather delicate species with tetrasporangia borne in short, clavate ultimate branchlets.

186a Medulla entirely composed of parenchyma type cells. Fig. 234...
....*Gracilaria foliifera*

Fig. 234. *Gracilaria foliifera*
(Forskal) Börgesen

Figure 234

An entire small plant showing the irregular branching in one plane, .× 0.64. This is a common and exceedingly variable plant ranging along the Atlantic Coast from Florida to Massachusetts in a variety of habitats, often in quiet, shallow water. It is our only common and widespread representative of a varied assemblage of flat species of *Gracilaria*, usually of subdichotomous branching. See step 23a for comments on cylindrical species of this genus.

186b Medulla composed of filamentous cells. Fig. 235...........187

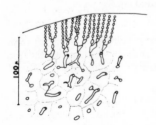

Figure 235

Fig. 235. *Grateloupia* sp.

A portion of a transection of a thallus to show the structure of filamentous type cells. The medullary cells are seen to be slender, often branched filaments loosely arranged in a jelly-like matrix.

187a Tetrasporangia borne in globose masses inside the cortex. Fig. 236..*Gigartina* (in part)

Fig. 236. *Gigartina canaliculata* Harvey

Part of a cystocarpic plant extracted from a clump, $\times$ 0.8. This is one of the commonest intertidal algae along the California coast, extending northward into Oregon. It is often a dominant member of rock-cover associations.

Another species which may best key out here is the Californian *G. leptorhynchos* J. Agardh which is of blackish color and provided with abundant, small, slender, spinose outgrowths on all surfaces.

For comments and illustrations of other forms of *Gigartina* see steps 151a and 168a.

Figure 236

187b Tetrasporangia not borne in globose masses inside the cortex but scattered and more or less solitary, or in nemathecia. Fig. 237..188

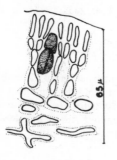

Fig. 237. *Grateloupia* sp.

One of the solitary, scattered tetrasporangia as found in this genus in contrast to the globose masses occurring in *Gigartina*.

Figure 237

188a Tetrasporangia borne in nemathecia; medulla prominent, densely stuffed with ramified filaments. Fig. 238....*Zanardinula* (in part)

Fig. 238. *Zanardinula lanceolata* (Harvey) J. De Toni

A small portion of an axis, × 0.8. This is perhaps the commonest and most widespread of the several species of this genus along the Pacific Coast. It occurs from southern California to northern Washington, and often reaches large, conspicuous size (35 cm.). Other common, non-dichotomous species from central California northward are Z. *andersoniana* (J. Agardh) Papenfuss and Z. *lyallii* (Harvey) J. De Toni, both of which have much broader, more ligulate blades.

Figure 238

188b Tetrasporangia scattered in the cortex (Fig. 237); medulla of loose filaments in a soft jelly. Figs. 235, 239.........*Grateloupia filicina*

Fig. 239. *Grateloupia filicina* (Wulfen) C. Agardh

An entire small plant of a rather broad form, × 0.8. This is an exceedingly variable species occurring in warm seas in many parts of the world. On our coasts it may be encountered from North Carolina southward and along the Gulf coast.

Figure 239

179

THE MARINE FLOWERING PLANTS

LTHOUGH the vast majority of seashore plants are algae, there are many localities along both the Atlantic and the Pacific coasts of the United States at which one will find at least one kind of flowering plant growing under strictly marine conditions in intertidal water or below. Sometimes these "sea grasses" may be so abundant as to form great beds on sand, mud or rocks to the virtual exclusion of other kinds of plants.

Inasmuch as there are only a few kinds of these "sea grasses" a key to them is unnecessary, and they may readily be identified by the use of the illustrations and notes which follow. Each of the common genera is illustrated. Only *Halophila* is omitted, for it may be encountered in quantity only in the Florida keys. Its species have small elliptical, petiolate leaves.

Fig. 240. *Zostera marina* Linnaeus (Eel Grass) A, B, C, $\times$ 0.5; D, $\times$ 1.

This is our most common and widespread marine flowering plant. It occurs along the Atlantic Coast from southern North Carolina northward, and, in favorable localities, along the entire Pacific Coast of the United States. It commonly lives on tidal mud flats and in bays and estuaries from low tide level down to twenty feet or more. The illustrations marked "A, B, C" show three variants of this species of which the narrow-leaf forms "A, B" are like those found along the Atlantic Coast and in some sheltered bays and estuaries along the Pacific. The large, broad-leaf form shown in "C" is known as *Zostera marina* var. *latifolia* Morong, and is the commoner form of Pacific shores. Along the open southern California coast it is often found on sandy bottoms in depths of fifteen feet or more. Fragments of the plants are commonly cast up on sandy beaches.

The flowers and fruits of eelgrass are rather obscure. Part of a fertile stem (spadix) is shown at "D," and two developing seeds are visible where the enveloping spathe does not completely cover them.

Because eelgrass is an important food plant of birds and of many marine animals along our coasts, it received a great deal of attention about twenty years ago. following its almost complete disappearance from the Atlantic Coast in 1931-32. The importance of this destructive "wasting disease" of *Zostera* led to much scientific research in an attempt to determine its cause, and although not proved, the most likely cause is now thought to have been a parasitic mycetozoan, *Labyrinthula*, living within its leaves. It took about fifteen years for the eelgrass to return to normal growth, apparently through the development of strains more resistant to the parasite.

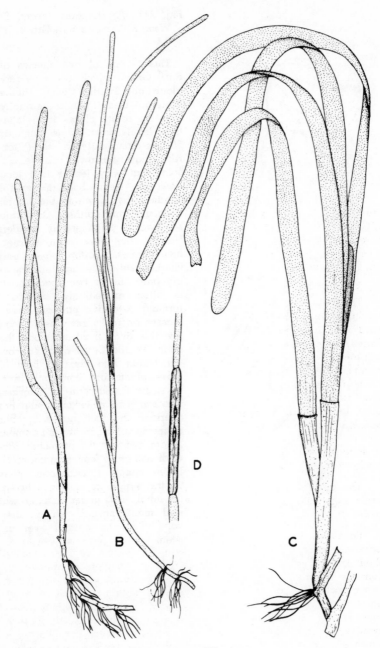

Figure 240

Figure 241

Fig. 241. *Phyllospadix torreyi* S. Watson (Torrey's Surf Grass) × 0.4.

This is one of two species of Surf Grass which occur widely along our Pacific Coast. Unlike *Zostera*, these plants normally grow in rocky places from intertidal levels down to as much as 50 feet along surfy shores. *P. torreyi* has narrow, compressed, somewhat wiry leaves and long flowering stems bearing several spadices as shown in the figure. It occurs from northern California southward. *Phyllospadix scouleri* Hooker, our only other species, has thinner, shorter leaves and short, basal flowering stems bearing only one or two spadices. It is often exceedingly abundant, forming extensive emerald green masses on rocky reefs near mean low tide line. It occurs along the entire Pacific Coast from Vancouver Island into Mexico. Both of these plants are commonly mistaken by the layman for eelgrass. The seaweed collector should not overlook the fact that a number of species of algae are to be found hidden beneath the protecting layer of surf grass leaves on the reefs. If one simply spreads and opens up the mantle of leaves to reveal the inhabitants under them, he will find many species which otherwise might be passed over unseen.

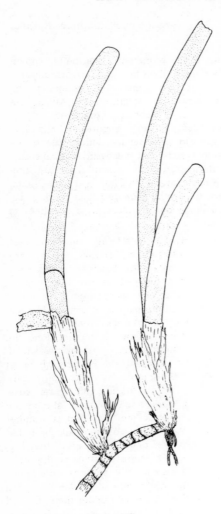

Figure 242

Fig. 242. *Thalassia testudinum* Koenig & Sims

(Turtle Grass), × 0.6.

This plant occurs in vast submarine fields around the Florida coasts, from near low tide level to as much as 35 feet. So abundant is it that in many places the leaves are washed ashore in sufficient quantities to be gathered for fertilizer. The rich vegetation of these marine meadows provide abundant food for marine animals, and in former times supported enormous numbers of sea turtles. The broad, straplike leaves distinguish it from the other marine seed plants of the Florida area. It occurs outside the range of *Zostera*, so need not be confused with that plant.

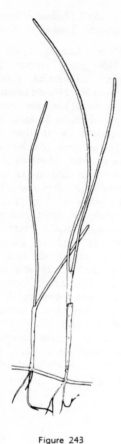

Figure 243

Fig. 243. *Syringodium filiforme* Kützing, × 0.56.

This is the Manatee Grass, better known in botanical literature, but incorrectly so, as *Cymodocea manatorum* Ascherson. The plant was first described by Kützing in 1863 from a specimen collected in the Virgin Islands and apparently mistaken for an alga. It occurs widely along the Florida coasts and westward to Louisiana. It often grows on infratidal sandy bottoms associated with *Thalassia* and *Diplanthera*, from which genera it is readily distinguished by its terete or semi-terete leaves.

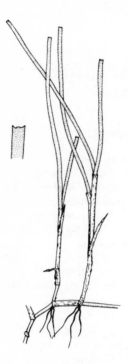

Figure 244

Fig. 244. *Diplanthera wrightii* (Ascherson) Ascherson, $\times$ 0.8.

This is another tropical species largely confined in our territory to the southern coasts of Florida. It occurs in shallow, quiet, often stagnant water, frequently in company with *Syringodium* and *Thalassia*. Its narrow flat leaves are distinctively truncate and toothed at the apex, as shown in the small inset figure.

PHYLOGENETIC LIST OF GENERA AND FAMILIES

GREEN ALGAE — CHLOROPHYTA

Ulotrichales

Ulotrichaceae
1. *Ulothrix*
   p. 75, fig. 96

Ulvaceae
2. *Monostroma*
   p. 71, fig. 88
3. *Ulva*
   p. 71, fig. 88
4. *Enteromorpha*
   p. 95, figs. 124, 125

Cladophorales

Cladophoraceae
5. *Chaetomorpha*
   pp. 76, 78; figs. 97, 100
6. *Urospora*
   p. 77, fig. 98
7. *Rhizoclonium*
   p. 77, fig. 99
8. *Spongomorpha*
   p. 78, fig. 101
9. *Cladophora*
   p. 79, fig. 102

Siphonales

Halicystidaceae
10. *Halicystis*
    p. 125, fig. 165

Valoniaceae
11. *Valonia*
    pp. 28, 75, 125, figs. 13, 95, 164
12. *Dictyosphaeria*
    p. 90, fig. 118

Siphonocladaceae
13. *Cladophoropsis*
    p. 80, fig. 103

Anadyomenaceae
14. *Anadyomene*
    p. 68, fig. 83

Caulerpaceae
15. *Caulerpa*
    pp. 72, 73, 145, 154, figs. 89, 90, 91, 188, 204

Bryopsidaceae
16. *Bryopsis*
    p. 73, fig. 92

Codiaceae
17. *Codium*
    p. 34, fig. 24
18. *Avrainvillea*
    p. 142, fig. 185
19. *Halimeda*
    p. 113, fig. 147
20. *Udotea*
    p. 119, figs. 155, 156
21. *Penicillus*
    p. 122, fig. 160
22. *Rhipocephalus*
    p. 123, fig. 161

Dasycladaceae
23. *Dasycladus*
    p. 74, fig. 93
24. *Batophora*
    p. 74, fig. 94
25. *Acetabularia*
    p. 120, fig. 158
26. *Neomeris*
    p. 121, fig. 159
27. *Cymopolia*
    p. 113, fig. 146

BROWN ALGAE — PHAEOPHYTA

RED ALGAE — RHODOPHYTA

INDEX AND PICTURED-GLOSSARY

Note that the numbers within parentheses following the generic names refer to the phylogenetic list of genera at which place the page and figure numbers are also given.

A

Acanthophora (No. 161) 62
 spicifera 62
ACCESSORY NUTRITIVE FILAMENTS: in the genus Gracilaria, those filaments which extend from the gonimoblast to the pericarp and which apparently serve as an accessory of nourishing the developing carpospores.
Acetabularia (No. 25) 120
 crenulata 120
Acrosorium (No. 155) 140
 uncinatum 140
Agardhiella (No. 113) 39
 coulteri 39
 tenera 39
Agarum (No. 56) 126
 cribrosum 126
 fimbriatum 126
Ahnfeltia (No. 124) 33
 concinna 33
 plicata 33
Alaria (No. 68) 137
 fistulosa 137
 marginata 137
Amphiroa (No. 106) 118
 fragilissima 118
 zonata 118
Anadyomene (No. 14) 68
 stellata 68
ANASTOMOSING: running together and fusing in such a way that the connections form a reticulation.
ANISOGAMOUS: having union of flagellated gametes of dissimilar size.
ANTICLINAL: perpendicular to the surface, as in the outer cortical cells in Fig. 245.

Figure 245

Antithamnion (No. 142) 83
APEX: (pl. APICES): the top or terminal end.
APICAL: at the apex.
ARCUATE: curved or bowed.
Ascophyllum (No. 72) 108
 nodosum 108
Asperococcus (No. 46) 96
 echinatus 96

Avrainvillea (No. 18) 142

B

Bangia (No. 81) 32
 fuscopurpurea 32
Batophora (No. 24) 74
 oerstedi 74
BLADE: that part of a thallus which is erect and more or less flattened or leaf-like.
Bonnemaisonia (No. 86) 61
 hamifera 61
 nootkana 61
Bossea (No. 101) 110, 114, 115
Botryocladia (No. 130) 100
 pseudodichotoma 100
Botryoglossum (No. 153) 135
 farlowianum 135
Bryopsis (No. 16) 73
 hypnoides 73
 pennata 73
 plumosa 73

C

CALCAREOUS: impregnated with calcium carbonate.
Calliarthron (No. 102) 115
 cheilosporioides 115
Callithamnion (No. 140) 49, 51, 52, 84, 85
 pikeanum 51
 rupicolum 84
Callophyllis (No. 111) 163
 marginifructa 163
CARPOGONIUM: the female sex organ in the Red Algae. In Fig. 246 a carpogonial branch (shaded) is shown from a cross section of a thallus of the Gracilariaceae. The carpogonium is the dilated portion of the uppermost cell. The slender, neck-like part is called the trichogyne.

Figure 246

CARPOSPOROPHYTE: that phase of the life history of a red alga arising directly or indirectly from the carpogonium and

borne on the female gametophyte. At maturity carpospores are produced from carposporangia on gonimoblast filaments.
Caulerpa (No. 15) 72, 73, 145, 154
 crassifolia 154
 fastigiata 72
 prolifera 145
 racemosa 72
 verticillata 72
Centroceras (No. 139) 56
 clavulatum 56
Ceramium (No. 138) 46, 47, 56, 57
 avalonae 47
 codicola 57
 eatonianum 57
 pacificum 57
 rubrum 57
Chaetomorpha (No. 5) 76, 78
 aerea 76
 antennina 76
 linum 78
 melagonium 76
 torta 78
Champia (No. 133) 94
 parvula 94
 salicornioides 94
CHLOROPLAST: the green, pigmented body or bodies within the cells of green algae.
Chondria (No. 159) 57, 63
 sedifolia 57
 tenuissima 63
Chondrus (No. 128) 161
 crispus 161
Chorda (No. 55) 37, 38
 filum 37, 38
 tomentosum 38
Chordaria (No. 39) 35
 dissessa 35
 flagelliformis 35
Cladophora (No. 9) 79
 albida 79
 trichotoma 79
Cladophoropsis (No. 13) 80
 membranacea 80
Codium (No. 17) 34
 dichotomum 34
 fragile 34
COENOCYTIC: consisting of one or more multinucleate cells. Coenocytic Green Algae may have frequent cell walls as in Chaetomorpha and Cladophora, or may be variously branched and ramified without cross walls in the filaments, as in Caulerpa and Bryopsis.
Coilodesme (No. 54) 93
 californica 93
 rigida 93
Colpomenia (No. 47) 91
 sinuosa 91
COMPLANATE: strongly flattened and more or less expanded.

192

COMPRESSED: somewhat flattened.

CONCEPTACLE: a cavity (either sunken or within a raised dome) with one or more openings to the thallus surface and bearing reproductive organs. Usage in the Red Algae is largely restricted to the family Corallinaceae.

Constantinea (No. 93) 141
  simplex 141

Corallina (No. 104) 117
  officinalis 117
  vancouveriensis 117

CORONATE: in the form of a crown; provided with a crown.

CORTEX: the outer tissue of a thallus external to the medulla and (or) the central axial filament and usually of smaller or shorter cells, some of which are pigmented. In Fig. 247 a cross section of a cylindrical red alga is shown in which a central axial filament is present within a large-celled medulla which in turn is surrounded by a small-celled cortex.

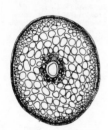

Figure 247

CORTICAL: pertaining to the cortex.

CORTICATED: provided with a cortex, often by secondary growth from the axis.

Costaria (No. 57) 129
  costata 129

Cryptonemia (No. 110) 152, 153
  obovata 152, 153

Cryptopleura (No. 154) 136
  violacea 136

CRYPTOSTOMATA: sunken cavities in a thallus (applied to certain Brown Algae) containing only hairs.

Cumagloia (No. 83)· 36
  andersonii 36

Cymodocea 184
  manatorum 184

Cymopolia (No. 27) 113
  barbata 113

CYSTOCARP: the "female" reproductive structure in most Red Algae. It con-

sists in the Florideae of carpospores and gonimoblast filaments, and, when the cystocarp protrudes from the surface of the thallus, of a special pericarp. The cystocarp may be deeply embedded in the thallus (as in Fig. 248) or emergent and protruding. One or more ostioles may be present.

Figure 248

Cystoclonium (No. 117) 65
  purpureum 65

Cystoseira (No. 77) 106
  osmundacea 106

D

Dasya (No. 157) 49, 50
  pacifica 50
  pedicellata 50

Dasycladus (No. 23) 74
  vermicularis 74

DECIDUOUS: falling off after a time.

Desmarestia (No. 45) 44, 139
  aculeata 139
  farcta 44
  media 44
  munda 139
  viridis 44

DETERMINATE BRANCHES: branches having a more or less definite limit to their length of growth.

DIAPHRAGM: a cellular partition across a hollow portion of a thallus.

DICHOTOMOUS: forked (usually repeatedly).

Dictyoneurum (No. 62) 128
  californicum 128

Dictyopteris (No. 32) 132
  delicatula 132
  justii 132
  plagiogramma 132
  polypodioides 132
  zonarioides 132

Dictyosiphon (No. 53) 65
  foeniculaceus 65

Dictyosphaeria (No. 12) 90
  cavernosa 90

Dictyota (No. 31) 162
  dichotoma 162
  flabellata 162

Digenia (No. 169) 54
  simplex 54

Diplanthera 185
  wrightii 185

DIPLOID: the condition in the life history of an alga in which each cell has

double the haploid number of chromosomes.

DISCOID: in the form of a disc.

DISTICHOUS: in two ranks.

DISTROMATIC: consisting of two layers of cells.

Dumontia (No. 90) 98
  incrassata 98

E

Ectocarpus (No. 28) 82

Egregia (No. 69) 104
  laevigata 104
  menziesii 104

Eisenia (No. 70) 155
  arborea 155

Elachista (No. 36) 81
  fucicola 81

Endarachne (No. 52) 148
  binghamiae 148

Endocladia (No. 95) 56, 60
  muricata 56, 60

Enteromorpha (No. 4) 95
  clathrata 95
  linza 95
  tubulosa 95

EPIPHYTIC: growing attached to another plant.

ESTIPITATE: without a stipe.

Eucheuma (No. 114) 40.
  isiforme 40

Eudesme (No. 43) 34
  virescens 34

F

Farlowia (No. 91) 174

Fauchea (No. 131) 166
  fryeana 166
  laciniata 166

FILAMENTS (cell form): the slender, elongated form assumed by certain cells, especially in the medulla of many Red Algae, Fig. 249.

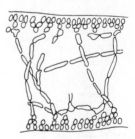

Figure 249

FLABELLATE: shaped more or less like a fan.

FLABELLUM: the fan-like portion of a thallus.

FLAGELLATED: provided with a flagellum.

FLAGELLUM: a whip-like process of protoplasm which provides locomotion for a motile cell.

H

HAIR: a unicellular or multicellular filament growing from the surface of a thallus. Fig. 250 shows a unicellular hair.

Figure. 250

I

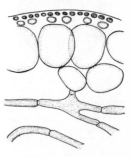

Figure 251

ISOGAMOUS: having union of gametes which are cf the same size.
ISOMORPHIC (alternation cf gentrations): similar in external form but not in essential structure.

J

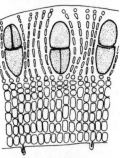

Figure 252

Figure 253

Figure 254

Figure 255

R

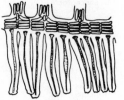

Figure 256

S

Figure 257

SESSILE: borne without a stipe or stalk.

SIMPLE: unbranched.

SOLITARY: consisting of only one; each one separate by itself.

SORUS (pl. sori): an aggregation of reproductive organs in a particular region or associated with some specilization of structure.

SPADIX: a kind of inflorescence in certain marine seed plants.

SPATHE: a large bract enclosing a spadix.

SPERMATIA: the non-motile male gametes of the Red Algae.

Spermothamnion (No. 145) 85, 87
  snyderae 87
  turneri 85, 87

Sphaerotrichia (No. 42) 59
  divaricata 59

Spongomorpha (No. 8) 78
  arcta 78
  coalita 78

SPOROPHYTE: in the life history of an alga, the asexual generation which produces diploid spores.

Spyridia (No. 136) 47
  aculeata 47
  filamentosa 47

STELLATE: provided with points like a star.

Stenogramme (No. 122) 164
  interrupta 164

Stilophora (No. 44) 37
  rhizoides 37

STIPE: the basal, stem-like part of a thallus beneath an erect blade.

STIPITATE: Borne on a stripe

STOLONIFEROUS: producing stolons.

STUPOSE: consisting of or provided with an abundance of rhizoids or hairs which may form a spongy mass.

SUB-: a prefix denoting a degree of, or an approach to, some quality; somewhat.

SYMPODIAL: a method of branching in which the leading apex is regularly and successively replaced by a branch from below which then assumes the terminal position for a time until in turn replaced.

Syringodium 184
  filiforme 184

T

TERETE: circular in transverse section.

TETRASPORANGIUM: an asexual reproductive structure in the Red Algae (Florideae) in which the divisions produce four spores (tetraspores), Fig. 258.

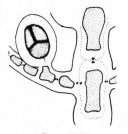

Figure 258

Thalassia 183
  testudinum 183

THALLUS: the entire plant body of an alga.

TRABECULAE: protuberances from the inside of the cell wall of species of *Caulerpa*.

TRANSECTION: a section cut crosswise.

TRICHOBLAST: a simple or branched, uniseriate, hairlike filament extending from the surface (usually at the tips) of certain red algae.

TRICHOTHALLIC: a manner of growth in which cell division occurs at the base of one or more apical hairs.

TRUNCATE: as though cut off at the end.

TUBERCULATE: warty.

U

Udotea (No. 20) 119
  flabellum 119

Ulothrix (No. 1) 75
  implexa 75

ULTIMATE: the last order.

Ulva (No. 3) 20, 21, 71

UNILATERAL: one-sided.

UNISERIATE: consisting of a single row of cells, either branched (Fig. 259), or unbranched.

UNIZONAL: consisting of a single zone or tier of cells.

Urospora (No. 6) 77
  penicilliformis 77

UTRICLE: a specialized, inflated, sac-like end of a filament of *Codium* of which the whole surface layer of the thallus is composed.

V

VACUOLATE: with scant contents within the cell cavity.

Valonia (No. 11) 28, 75, 125
  aegagropila 75
  ventricosa 28, 125

VERTICILLATE: whorled.

VESICLE: an air bladder or float.

W

WHORLS: verticils or circles of branches or organs about an axis.

Wrangelia (No. 137) 51
  penicillata 51

Z

Zanardinula (No. 109) 160, 179
  andersoniana 179
  cornea 160
  lanceolata 179
  lvallii 179

Zonaria (No. 35) 134
  farlowii 134

Zostera 180
  marina 180
  marina var. *latifolia* 180

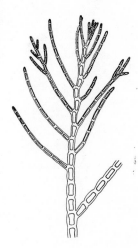

Figure 259